Selected Calculations in Electric Power

Selected Calculations in Electric Power

T. P. Allen M.Sc., C.Eng., F.I.E.E.
Electrical Engineering Department,
The Queen's University, Belfast.

R. E. Steven B.Sc., Ph.D., C.Eng., F.I.E.E.
Electrical Engineering Department,
The University, Southampton.

HODDER AND STOUGHTON
LONDON SYDNEY AUCKLAND TORONTO

British Library Cataloguing in Publication Data

Allen, T P
    Selected calculations in electric power.
    1. Electric engineering – Mathematics
    2. Electric engineering – Problems, exercises, etc.
    I. Title   II. Steven, Robert Edgar
    621.3'01'51   TK168

    ISBN 0-340-24359-7

First published 1979

Printed in Great Britain for
Hodder and Stoughton Educational,
A division of Hodder and Stoughton Ltd.,
Mill Road, Dunton Green, Sevenoaks, Kent.
by Biddles Ltd., Guildford, Surrey
Typeset by Alden Press Ltd.,
Oxford, London and Northampton.

Contents

To

Thomas Palmer Allen

Professor Emeritus

My good friend and teacher, "T.P." Allen died
shortly before the publication date of this book.

Robert E. Steven
Southampton, March, 1979.

Preface

Calculations to a student of electrical engineering can mean correct answers to typical examination questions. To a practising engineer they represent the application of methods of theoretical analysis to the solution of a particular problem. The skill with which either individual will tackle a problem will depend both upon his understanding of basic principles and upon his experience in applying these principles to typical situations.

Because of the increasing complexity and variety of applications of electrical engineering theory, many college syllabuses have had to be constrained to emphasise fundamentals, with a consequent reduction in the time available for solving problems. A similar influence has become apparent in a number of otherwise excellent contemporary textbooks.

In this book the Authors present a selection of worked problems. Many of these are based upon examination questions, sometimes modified in statement and extended in solution to emphasise particular aspects of theory or forms of solution. The modification may reflect a preferred mathematical form for use with a computer, or possibly emphasise a notable relationship not normally evident in the theory. Problems are included relating to conventional and generalised theory, steady-state and dynamic performance of electrical machines and power systems and apparatus.

The references given are generally available textbooks of recent date, but of course are not the only suitable references. It is hoped that students will become acquainted with other references in the field of study and thereby become more secure in their understanding of electrical engineering.

The Authors wish to thank the Senates of the Queens University, Belfast, and of Southampton University for their kind permission to use examples from past examination papers, directly or in abridged form. In addition they acknowledge with thanks guidance obtained from various papers and textbooks. These are hopefully all identified, directly or indirectly, in the limited list of references given.

Units and Symbols

In this book rationalised m.k.s. units are implied except where specifically stated otherwise. In general, two basic systems of units are found in engineering practice, namely metric and English units.

The adoption of an International System of Units, (SI units), is recommended, (Ref. 17). This practical system of units adopts base units relating to the measurement of six quantities: length, mass, time, electric current, thermodynamic temperature and luminous intensity. Units of related quantities are derived coherently, i.e. using unity as the multiplying factor. The principal chosen units can provide a terminology "m.k.s.A" units using a mass-based system, with unit mass, (1 kilogram), as a basis giving the SI unit of force as the newton. The SI system does not use an m.k.s. unit of force based upon concepts of weight, (i.e. the kilogram-weight), since this depends upon the value of acceleration due to gravity, which is not constant.

However, the recommendation does not protect students from variations which occur in practice and some definitions, discussion and conversion factors are given below.

Mechanical Units

Since force = mass × acceleration, we have the following definitions;

Metric

SI units (m.k.s. mass-based)

mass	acceleration	force	work & energy	power
1 kg	1 m/s^2	1 newton (= 10^5 dyne)	1 joule = 1 newton.metre	1 watt = 1 joule/s

Adoption of the SI unit system is recommended to secure a greater degree of uniformity and understanding in the use of units. Other units are generally deprecated, unless there are good reasons for their use, (e.g. in theoretical physics)

m.k.s. units (force-based)

mass	acceleration	force	work & energy	power
1 kg	$9.807 \, \text{m/s}^2$	1 kg(f) $= 9.807 \, \text{N}$	1 kg(f) m	1 metric hp $= 75 \, \text{kg(f)m/s}$ $= 736 \, \text{watt}$ $= 1 \, \text{pferde-stärke}$ $= 1 \, \text{cheval-vapeur}$

c.g.s. units, (mass-based)

1 g	$1 \, \text{cm/s}^2$	1 dyne	1 erg	1 erg/s

c.g.s. units, (force-based)

1 g	$980.7 \, \text{cm/s}^2$	1 g(f)

English

f.p.s. units, (mass-based)

1 lb	$1 \, \text{ft/s}^2$	1 poundal

f.p.s. units, (force-based)

1 lb	$32.18 \, \text{ft/s}^2$	1 lb(f) $(= 4.45 \, \text{N})$	1 ft lb	550 ft lb/s $= 1 \, \text{hp}$ $= 746 \, \text{watt}$
1 slug	$1 \, \text{ft/s}^2$	1 lb(f)		

Electrical Units

Interpretation of electrical phenomena is somewhat obscured by the practice of using commemorative names for significant units. To relate these units to the more familiar mechanical dimensions we may, (i) define the force between unit charges, or (ii) more practically, measure the force between two parallel current-carrying conductors. Hence the SI unit of electric current, the ampere, is defined, (Ref. 17),

'The ampere is that constant current which, if maintained in two straight parallel conductors of infinite length, of negligible circular cross-section, and placed 1 metre apart in vacuum, would produce between these conductors a force equal to 2×10^{-7} newton per metre of length.'

When we adopt the rationalised m.k.s.A system of units we have,

$$F = \frac{\mu_0 I_1 I_2 l}{2\pi d} \text{ newton}$$

and the currents are measured in amperes.

This is not a simple relationship because it involves the concept of permeability of free space, μ_0, and the constant 2π due to the adoption of 'rationalisation'.

An alternative approach introduces the idea of a magnetic field of density B and the electro-magnetic force law, viz;

$$F = Bli \text{ newton}, \quad \text{for a conductor of length } l$$

Then work done in advancing a distance x across the field,

$$W = Blix \text{ joule}$$

Now

$$Blx = \text{total flux crossing the area } (l \times x)$$

The m.k.s.A unit of magnetic flux is the weber, (Wb). Thus

$$1 \text{ weber} = 1 \text{ joule/amp} = 1 \text{ newton.metre/amp}$$

The m.k.s.A unit of flux density is the tesla = weber/m^2 and hence

$$1 \text{ tesla} = \left(\frac{\text{joule}}{\text{amp}}\right)\left(\frac{1}{\text{metre}^2}\right) = \frac{\text{newton}}{\text{ampere.metre}}$$

The law for electro-magnetic induction can be stated,

$$\text{Voltage} = Blv, \quad \text{where } v = \text{velocity across field}$$

Substituting from above,

$$\text{Voltage} = \left(\frac{\text{newton}}{\text{ampere.metre}}\right)(\text{metre})\left(\frac{\text{metre}}{\text{sec}}\right) = \text{joule/coulomb}$$

and

$$\text{Power} = \text{volt} \times \text{amp} = \left(\frac{\text{joule}}{\text{coulomb}}\right)\left(\frac{\text{coulomb}}{\text{sec}}\right) = \text{watt}$$

Now we refer to (ii) above, and substituting dimensions,

$$\text{newton} = \frac{\mu_0 (\text{amp})^2 (\text{metre})}{2\pi (\text{metre})}$$

whence μ_0 has dimensions newton/amp^2 and a magnitude of $4\pi \times 10^{-7}$ m.k.s. units, (also henry/metre, and in dimensional notation $[MLQ^{-2}]$).

Referring to (i), the force between charges is defined,

$$F = \frac{q_1 q_2}{4\pi r^2 \epsilon_0} \text{ newton}$$

ϵ_0 is termed the permittivity of free space, with dimensions

$$\frac{(\text{coulomb})^2}{(\text{newton})(\text{metre})^2} \quad \text{and magnitude } 8.85 \times 10^{-12} \text{ m.k.s. units}$$

(also farad/metre, and in dimensional notation $[M^{-1}L^{-3}T^2Q^2]$).

The physical constants are interrelated thus,

$$c = \frac{1}{\sqrt{(\mu_0 \epsilon_0)}} = 3 \times 10^8 \text{ m/sec} = \text{Velocity of light}$$

Other useful physical constants are:

$$\text{Mass of an electron} = 9.1 \times 10^{-31} \text{ kg}$$

$$\text{Electron charge} = 1.603 \times 10^{-19} \text{ coulomb}$$

Conversion Factors

Length	1 metre (m)	$= 3.281$ feet (ft)
		$= 39.37$ inch (in)
Mass	1 kilogram (kg)	$= 2.205$ pound (lb)
		$= 35.27$ ounce (oz)
		$= 0.0685$ slug
Force	1 newton (N)	$= 10^5$ dyne
		$= 0.2248$ pound (lbf)
		$= 7.233$ poundal
Energy	1 joule (J)	$= 10^7$ erg
		$= 1$ watt sec (W.s)
		$= 0.7376$ foot pound (ft lb)
		$= 0.2388$ calorie
		$= 9.48 \times 10^{-4}$ BTU
	(1 calorie	$= 4.186$ joule)
Power	1 watt (W)	$= \frac{1}{746} = 1.341 \times 10^{-3}$ hp
		$= 0.7376$ ft lb/sec

Magnetic flux

1 weber (Wb)	$= 10^8$ maxwell (lines)
	$= 10^5$ kiloline

Magnetic flux density

1 tesla (T)	$= 1\,\text{Wb/m}^2$
	$= 10^4$ gauss
	$= 64.52$ kiloline/in^2

Magneto-motive-force

1 ampere	$= 1.257$ gilbert

Magnetic field intensity

1 amp/metre	$= 2.54 \times 10^{-2}$ A/in
	$= 1.257 \times 10^{-2}$ oersted

List of Symbols

The symbols used in this book are of common conventional usage, but the same symbol may be employed in two different contexts. The following list is provided for general guidance, in addition to local definitions within the text.

A	amplifier gain; a constant
A	ampere (unit of current)
AT	ampere-turns
a	armature; a dimension
a	parallel paths of a winding
B	flux density, (tesla = weber/metre^2)
B	a phase axis
b	a dimension; base terminal
C	capacitance (farad)
c	velocity of light; collector terminal
cu	copper
D	diameter; damping coefficient
D_e	effective damping
d	a distance; differential; unidirectional
d	direct axis
E	r.m.s. and d.c. voltage
e	instantaneous voltage; electron charge
e	emitter terminal; electrical
F	force (newton); farad (unit of capacitance)
f	instantaneous force; frequency (hertz = cycles/sec)

f	field quantity; function of
G	transfer function; generator; conductance
G	rotational inductance coefficient $= dM/d\theta$
g	gram; generator quantity
H	magnetising force (ampere turns)
H	henry (unit of inductance)
h	hysteresis quantity; hours
hp	horse power, (1 hp $=$ 746 watt)
I	r.m.s. current, d.c. current; $I^* =$ conjugate phasor I
i	instantaneous current
J	polar moment of inertia
j	mathematical operator $= (-1)^{1/2}$
K	a constant
k	kilo $= 10^3$ unit
k	transformation ratio; a constant
L	inductance (henry)
L	length; suffix for Line value; suffix for Load
l	length
M	mass (kilogram); mutual inductance (henry)
m	number of phases
m	milli $= 10^{-3}$ unit
m	metre; mass; motor quantity; mechanical
m or max	maximum value
N	newton; a number; speed in r.p.m.; phases of a rectifier
n	speed in rev/sec
0	origin of a graph
o	subscript for No Load; output quantity
P	power (watt); line propagation constant $= (\alpha + j\beta)$
p	differential operator d/dt
p	pairs of poles
ph	per phase
pu	per unit
Q	kilovolt-amperes reactive, (also termed VAR)
q	quadrature axis
q	charge (coulomb)
R	ohmic resistance; a phase axis
r	a radius; ohmic resistance; a rotor quantity
S	area; complex power $= P + jQ = VI^*$
s	fractional slip; complex frequency; seconds, (unit of time)
s	suffix for stator; synchronous; source
T	time constant (seconds); time; turns; tesla, (unit of flux density)
Ⓣ	torque (newton-metre)

t	time; terminal value
V	r.m.s. or d.c. voltage
V	unit of voltage
v	instantaneous velocity; voltage
W	energy (joule or watt.sec)
W	power (watt)
Wb	weber, (unit of flux)
X	reactance
x	displacement; dimension; algebraic term
x	Steinmetz index
Y	admittance; a phase axis
y	admittance; an algebraic term
Z	electrical impedance; number of conductors
z_m	impedance in mechanical units

Greek symbols

α	impedance angle $= \tan^{-1} R/X$
α	real part of complex root; damping factor; attenuation
α	delay angle of rectifier.
β	a measure of damping $= (1 - \zeta^2)^{1/2}$
β	an angle; inverter angle of advance; phase shift
δ	an angle
δ	load angle; inverter extinction angle
ϵ	exponential function, base of natural logarithms
ϵ	permittivity
ζ	damping ratio
η	efficiency
θ	an angle; a temperature; $\dot{\theta} = d\theta/dt =$ rotational speed, rad/sec
λ	impedance angle $= \tan^{-1} X/R$
λ	operator for $120°$ phase shift; overlap angle
μ	micro $= 10^{-6}$ unit; permeability
ε	error
π	mathematical constant
Σ	summation
Φ	magnetic flux (weber $=$ tesla.metre^2)
ϕ	instantaneous magnetic flux; phase angle
ψ	mechanical angle
ω	angular frequency; speed, in rad/sec
Δ	a determinant; a small change
∂	partial differential

Chapter One
Devices

Example 1

Design an inductor of nominal inductance 10 mH and rated for a current of maximum value 15 amp. Assume that the inductor is built using a standard laminated silicon–iron 'C' core, (comprising 2 C-shaped cores butted together to form an O-shape). The core chosen has effective cross-section at each air-gap of 9.2 cm² and recommended max flux density of 1.5 Wb/m². Check the suitability of the core, using approximate current rating for the conductor of 150 A/cm² and core window-space area of 30 cm².

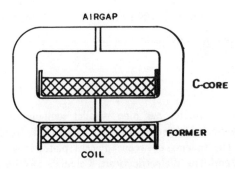

AIRGAP

C-CORE

FORMER

COIL

Fig. 1

Solution

Working from first principles, energy stored in an inductance,

$$W = \tfrac{1}{2}Li^2$$

Assuming all energy is stored in the airgaps, (i.e. $\mu_{\text{iron}} \gg 1$) then

$$W = \frac{B_m^2}{2\mu_0} \quad \text{(volume of airgap)}$$

Equating these expressions, and substituting given figures,

$$\text{Volume of airgap} = \frac{(Li^2)\mu_0}{B_m^2} = \frac{10 \times 10^{-3} \times 15^2 \times 4\pi \times 10^{-7}}{(1.5)^2}$$

$$= 4\pi \times 10^{-7}\,\text{m}^3 = 1.257\,\text{ccs}$$

Core chosen has cross-section $= 9.2\,\text{cm}^2$.

$$\therefore \qquad \text{Length of airgap required} = \frac{1.257}{9.2} = 1.37\,\text{mm}$$

This would be obtained by placing non-magnetic spacers at the butt joints each of thickness $= 1.37/2 = 0.69\,\text{mm}$.

Now Amp-turns required on the airgaps $= B_m l/\mu_0$

$$= \frac{1.5 \times 1.37 \times 10^{-3}}{4\pi \times 10^{-7}} = \frac{2.055 \times 10^4}{4\pi}$$

$$= 1635$$

Hence turns required $= 1635/15 = 109$ turns.

Check on window space:

$$\text{Cross-section per conductor at } 15\,\text{A} = 10\,\text{mm}^2 \text{ copper}$$

$$\text{Nett c.s.a. of copper in 109 turns} = 109 \times 10\,\text{mm}^2 = 10.9\,\text{cm}^2$$

This allows ample space for insulation and winding space in the given window area of $30\,\text{cm}^2$.

Example 2

An electrostatic voltmeter has nine parallel semi-circular plates, alternate plates being connected together. One set of plates is fixed, the other set is free to move. The spacing between adjacent plates is 4 mm, and the plate diameter is 10 cm. The dielectric is air. Calculate (a) the total capacitance when the plates overlap by one radian, (b) the stiffness of suspension necessary to permit a rotation of $120°$ for an applied voltage to the plates of $1000\,\text{V}$.

Solution

Part (a).   For a parallel-plate capacitor,

$$\text{Capacitance}, C = (\epsilon_r \epsilon_0 S)/d \quad \text{farad}$$

where

ϵ_r = relative permittivity of dielectric

ϵ_0 = permittivity of air = $8.854 \times 10^{-12}\,\text{F/m}$

S = area of overlap of plates in $(\text{metre})^2$

d = thickness of dielectric in metres

For a multi-plate capacitor, (with air dielectric, $\epsilon_r = 1$)

$$C = \frac{\epsilon_0(N-1)S}{d} \text{ farad,}$$

where N = number of plates and $(N-1)$ = number of dielectrics.
For the given device, $(N-1) = 8$.

$$\therefore \quad C = \frac{8\epsilon_0 S}{d} = \frac{8 \times (8.854 \times 10^{-12}) \times (1/2\pi)(\pi/4)(10^{-2})}{4 \times 10^{-3}}$$

$$= 22.2 \times 10^{-12} \text{ farad/radian overlap}$$

Part (b).   Let k = control-spring torque constant = $\widehat{T}/\theta$ Nm/rad. For a small deflection $d\theta$ due to torque $\widehat{T}$,

$$\text{Work done} = \widehat{T}\,d\theta$$

Now,

$$\text{energy stored in a capacitor, } W = \tfrac{1}{2}CV^2$$

$$\text{Differential stored energy, } dW = \tfrac{1}{2}V^2\,dC \quad \text{for change in } C$$

$$= \widehat{T}\,d\theta$$

$$\widehat{T} = \tfrac{1}{2}V^2\,\frac{dC}{d\theta}$$

and

$$k = \frac{1}{2\theta}(V^2)\frac{dC}{d\theta}$$

Now,

$$C = \frac{8\epsilon_0 S}{d} = \frac{8\epsilon_0}{d}\left(\frac{\pi}{4}\right)D^2\,\frac{\theta}{2\pi}$$

where θ = overlap angle and D = plate diameter.

$$\therefore \quad \frac{dC}{d\theta} = \frac{\epsilon_0 D^2}{d} = \frac{8.854 \times 10^{-12} \times 0.01}{4 \times 10^{-3}} = 2.213 \times 10^{-11}$$

Hence

$$\text{Stiffness, } k = \frac{10^6 \times 2.213 \times 10^{-11}}{2(2\pi/3)} = 5.29 \times 10^{-6} \text{ Nm/rad}$$

Example 3

Derive an expression for the deflection sensitivity of a cathode ray tube. Hence calculate the deflection for 10 volt applied to the y-deflection plates, for a tube specified as follows: distance from deflection plates to the screen, $L = 25$ cm, length of deflection plate, $l = 4$ cm, distance between deflection plates, $d = 1$ cm. The forward accelerating potential from the cathode to the deflection plates = 2500 volt. Assume that the screen is at the same potential as the point where electrons leave the influence of the plates.

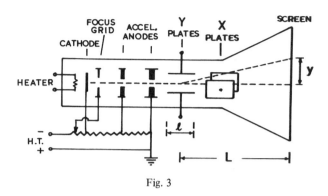

Fig. 3

Solution

The deflection axes, perpendicular to the tube axis, are termed x and y axes, and the direction of the tube axis, z. Now, as a charged particle falls through an electric field the particle loses potential energy as it gains kinetic energy. Assuming the particle has constant mass, m,

$$\therefore \qquad qV_z = \tfrac{1}{2}mv_z^2$$

Then,

$$v_z = \left(\frac{2qV_z}{m}\right)^{1/2}$$

Transit time through deflection plates of length l,

$$t = \frac{l}{v_z} = l\left(\frac{m}{2qV_z}\right)^{1/2}$$

Let V_y = voltage between deflection plates, spaced at d. Then

$$\text{transverse electric field gradient} = \frac{V_y}{d}$$

$$F_y = \frac{qV_y}{d} = ma_y \quad \text{where } a_y = \text{transverse acceleration}$$

Hence,

$$v_y = a_y t$$

$$= \left(\frac{qV_y}{md}\right) \times l\left(\frac{m}{2qV_z}\right)^{1/2} = \frac{lV_y}{d}\left(\frac{q}{2mV_z}\right)^{1/2}$$

Assuming constant axial and transverse velocities after leaving the plates, then by similar triangles,

$$\frac{y}{v_y} = \frac{L}{v_z} \quad \text{or} \quad y = L\frac{v_y}{v_z}$$

Substituting for v_y and v_z from above,

$$\therefore \quad y = L\left[\frac{lV_y}{d}\left(\frac{q}{2mV_z}\right)^{1/2}\right]\bigg/\left(\frac{2qV_z}{m}\right)^{1/2}$$

$$= \frac{LlV_y}{2dV_z}$$

Deflection sensitivity $= \dfrac{Ll}{2dV_z}$ metre/volt on deflection plates

The numerical part is

$$y = \frac{(25 \times 10^{-2})(4 \times 10^{-2}) \times 10}{2 \times (1 \times 10^{-2}) \times 2500} \text{ metre}$$

$$= 0.2 \text{ cm}$$

Example 4

A cathode ray tube has a coaxial solenoid wound about it. The coil produces a uniform magnetic field directed along the axis, of uniform density 0.01 Wb/m² across the tube section. Electrons emitted through a small aperture in the anode, have axial velocity towards the screen of 6×10^7 m/sec and a maximum transverse velocity of 10^6 m/sec. Estimate the size of the spot on the screen distant 30 cm from the anode. For an electron take $e/m = 1.76 \times 10^{11}$ C/kg.

Solution

In general, for an electric charge, q, moving with velocity v in a magnetic field of density B, the force exerted on the charge is given,

$$\mathbf{F} = q(\mathbf{v} \times \mathbf{B})$$

and $\mathbf{F}, \mathbf{v}$ and $\mathbf{B}$ are mutually at right angles.

For the given problem, Fig. 4, a force acts on an electron of charge $(-e)$, due to transverse velocity v_r, given as

$$F_\theta = -ev_rB_z$$

where F_θ is $\perp v_r$ and causes motion in a circle. But the electron also moves axially to the screen due to v_z. Hence the motion is in a helix.

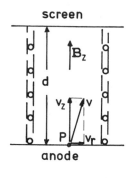
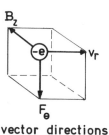

anode   vector directions

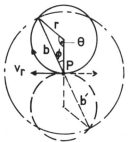

Fig. 4

$$\text{Constant circular acceleration} = \frac{F_\theta}{m} = \frac{e v_r B_z}{m}$$

This is also equal to $\omega^2 r = v_r^2/r$ where $\omega = v_r/r =$ angular velocity.

$$\therefore \qquad r = \frac{v_r}{(e/m) B_z}$$

$$= \frac{10^6}{(1.76 \times 10^{11}) \times 0.01} = 0.568 \text{ mm}$$

for an electron having maximum transverse velocity. Now,

$$\text{transit time to screen} = \frac{d}{v_z} = \frac{0.3}{6 \times 10^7} = 5 \times 10^{-9} \text{ sec}$$

Time to complete 1 loop of helix

$$= \frac{2\pi r}{v_r} = \frac{2\pi \times 0.568 \times 10^{-3}}{10^6} = 3.57 \times 10^{-9}$$

Hence the electron completes $5/3.57 = 1.4$ loops.

Referring to Fig. 4 the electron strikes the screen at a *radial* distance 'b' from its starting point P. But electrons will leave the anode with transverse velocities in the opposite and other directions. Hence 'b' is the radius of the spot on the screen.

We have,

$$\theta = 0.4 \times 360° = 144°$$

$$\phi = \tfrac{1}{2}(180° - 144°) = 18°$$

$$\therefore \qquad b = 2r \cos \phi = 2 \times 0.568 \times \cos 18°$$

$$= 1.08 \, \text{mm}$$

N.B. It may be of interest to check the 'relativistic' change in mass at this speed, viz;

If mass of electron at rest $= m_0$, then mass when moving at velocity v is,

$$m = \frac{m_0}{[1 - (v^2/c^2)]^{1/2}}$$

In the given case, $v = 6 \times 10^7$ m/sec, also $c = 3 \times 10^8$ m/sec. Hence

$$m = \frac{m_0}{\left(1 - \dfrac{36 \times 10^{14}}{9 \times 10^{16}}\right)^{1/2}} = \left(\frac{900}{864}\right)^{1/2} m_0$$

$$= 1.021 m_0$$

that is, a 2.1% increase, which may be neglected.

Example 5

A circuit current is defined as a sinusoidal a.c. superimposed on a direct current. A moving-coil meter connected in series indicates 8 amp and a moving-iron meter indicates 11 amp. Calculate the current indicated by the moving-iron meter if the d.c. component of current is reduced to zero.

Solution

The moving-coil meter reads the average current $= 8$ amp.
The moving-iron meter reads the root-mean-square value $= 11$ amp.
Now

$$\text{instantaneous current} = i = (8 + I_{\text{max}} \sin \omega t)$$

$$i^2 = (8 + I_{\text{max}} \sin \omega t)^2 = 64 + 16 I_{\text{max}} \sin \omega t + I_{\text{max}}^2 \sin^2 \omega t$$

Average of i^2

$$= \frac{1}{2\pi} \int_0^{2\pi} (64 + 16I_{max} \sin \omega t + I_{max}^2 \sin^2 \omega t) \, d\omega t$$

$$= \frac{1}{2\pi} \int_0^{2\pi} \left(64 + 16I_{max} \sin \omega t + \frac{I_{max}^2}{2} - \frac{I_{max}^2}{2} \cos 2\omega t \right) d\omega t$$

$$= \frac{1}{2\pi} \left[64\omega t - 16I_{max} \cos \omega t + \frac{I_{max}^2}{2} \omega t - \frac{I_{max}^2}{4} \sin 2\omega t \right]_0^{2\pi}$$

$$= \frac{1}{2\pi} \left[64(2\pi) - 16I_{max} + \frac{I_{max}^2}{2} (2\pi) - \frac{I_{max}^2}{4} (0) - 0 + 16I_{max} - 0 + 0 \right]$$

$$= 64 + \frac{I_{max}^2}{2}$$

Hence

$$\text{r.m.s. value of } i = \left[64 + \frac{I_{max}^2}{2} \right]^{1/2} = 11$$

$$\therefore \qquad I_{max}^2 = 114$$

$$I_{max} = 10.68 \text{ amp}$$

If the d.c. component is reduced to zero, the moving-iron meter will read the r.m.s. value of a sine waveform of maximum value 10.68 amps.

Hence the meter indication will be $10.68/\sqrt{2} = 7.553$ say 7.55 amp.

Example 6

An electromechanical vibrator has a cylindrical moving coil of 100 turns and mean diameter 1.4 cm. The coil element is constrained to permit movement axially in a concentric radial magnetic field at an effective flux density of 0.5 Wb/m². The coil element has a mass of 2.4 g, the constraint has axial stiffness of 3000 N/m and viscous damping is 0.12 N sec/m.

(a) Using analogue principles show that the motional impedance can be represented by an electrical circuit and calculate the values of the equivalent electrical components.

(b) Prove that a frequency locus of the motional impedance will be a circle.

Solution (Ref. 2. p. 40)

Part (a). The device may be symbolised as in Fig. 6(a). A time-dependent equation for the electrical part is,

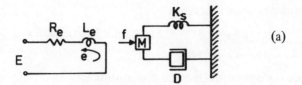

(a)

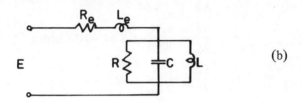

(b)

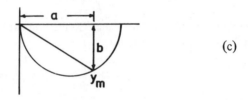

(c)

Fig. 6

$$L_e \, di/dt + iR_e + e = E$$

where $e = Blv = K_0 v$ and K_0 is termed the 'transduction factor'.

For the mechanical part; D = viscous damping, K_s = spring constant then,

$$M \, dv/dt + Dv + K_s \int v \, dt = f = Bli = K_0 i \,.$$

Note that there is a unique relationship between the electrical and mechanical variables. Substituting for v in terms of e,

$$\frac{M}{K_0^2} \frac{de}{dt} + \frac{D}{K_0^2} e + \frac{K_s}{K_0^2} \int e \, dt = i$$

This equation is analogous to that for a node circuit of R, L and C in parallel, viz., Fig. 6(b)

$$C \frac{de}{dt} + \frac{e}{R} + \frac{1}{L} \int e \, dt = i$$

Substituting numerical values,

$$K_0 = Bl = 0.5(\pi \times 1.4 \times 10^{-2} \times 100) = 2.2$$
$$K_0^2 = 4.84$$

Hence the equivalent electrical components are,

$$C = \frac{M}{K_0^2} = \frac{2.4 \times 10^{-3}}{4.84} = 500 \times 10^{-6} \text{ farad}$$

$$L = \frac{K_0^2}{K_s} = \frac{4.84}{3000} = 1.61 \times 10^{-3} \text{ henry}$$

$$R = \frac{K_0^2}{D} = \frac{4.84}{0.12} = 40.3 \text{ ohm}$$

Part (b).   In operational notation,

$$Z_{\text{mot}} = \frac{e}{i} = K_0^2 \bigg/ \left(Mp + D + \frac{K_s}{p}\right) = K_0^2/z_m$$

where z_m = mechanical impedance (Ref. 2 and Paper 4).

In frequency-response terms,

$$z_m = j\omega M + D + \frac{K_s}{j\omega} = D + j\left(\omega M - \frac{K_s}{\omega}\right)$$

$$= D + jX_m \quad \text{(say)}$$

$$\therefore \qquad y_m = \frac{1}{D + jX_m} = \frac{D - jX_m}{D^2 + X_m^2} = a - jb, \quad \text{Fig. 6(c)}$$

Then,

$$\text{magnitude } |y_m| = (a^2 + b^2)^{1/2}$$

$$= \left[\left(\frac{D}{D^2 + X_m^2}\right)^2 + \left(\frac{X_m}{D^2 + X_m^2}\right)^2\right]^{1/2}$$

$$= \left[\frac{1}{D^2 + X_m^2}\right]^{1/2} = (a/D)^{1/2}$$

Hence

$$(a^2 + b^2) = a/D$$

This can be written,

$$\left(a - \frac{1}{2D}\right)^2 + b^2 = \frac{1}{4D^2}$$

which is the equation of a circle of radius $1/2D$ with centre $(1/2D, 0)$

N.B.   When $\omega M = K_s/\omega$ or $\omega = (K_s/M)^{1/2}$, then $y_m = 1/D$ which defines the resonant point, on the 'real' axis. In electrical terms, $Z_{mot} = K_0^2(y_m)$ where K_0^2 is a constant scale factor. Hence the locus obtained from a frequency response test on the device will be a circle of diameter $= K_0^2(1/D) = R$.

Example 7

(a) Define the 'quadrantal frequencies' and show how they are employed in the derivation of the constants of an electromechanical transducer. (b) Experimental values obtained from electrical impedance measurements carried out on an electromechanical vibrator unit are given in Fig. 7. Determine the values of the mechanical constants of the unit, given that when a mass of 13 g is added to the moving part a new value of resonant frequency occurs $= 885$ rad/sec.

Solution (Ref. 2, p. 43)

Part (a).   The terminal electrical impedance of the unit can be expressed,

$$Z_t = Z_e + \frac{K_0^2}{z_m}$$

where $Z_e =$ inherent electrical impedance, (when clamped).

$$\frac{K_0^2}{z_m} = Z_{mot} = \text{motional impedance in electrical units,}$$

where K_0 is the 'transduction factor' and z_m is the mechanical impedance of the moving part in mechanical units.

Representing the motional impedance by an equivalent circuit of R, L and C in parallel, (see Ex. 6), we have,

$$Y_{mot} = \frac{1}{R} + j\left(\omega C - \frac{1}{\omega L}\right)$$

Then

$$Z_{mot} = \frac{1}{Y_{mot}} = \frac{R}{1 + jR\left(\omega C - \frac{1}{\omega L}\right)}$$

$$= \frac{R - jR^2\left(\omega C - \frac{1}{\omega L}\right)}{1 + R^2\left(\omega C - \frac{1}{\omega L}\right)^2} \quad \text{by rationalizing}$$

(a)

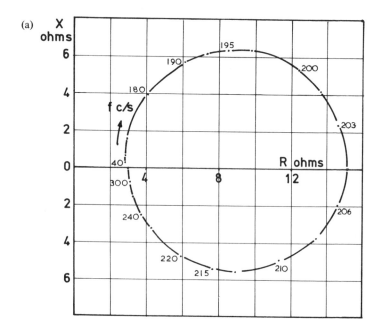

(b)

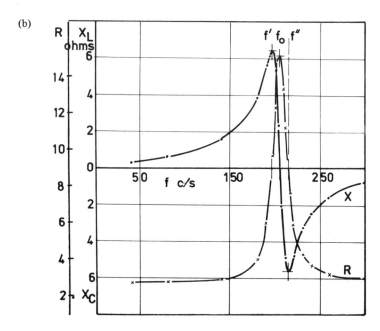

Fig. 7 (a) and (b)

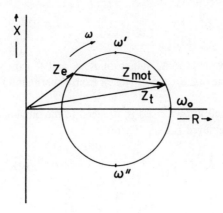

Fig. 7(c)

At resonance the j-component is zero, and resonant frequency ω_0 is given by,

$$\omega_0 C = \frac{1}{\omega_0 L} \quad \text{whence} \quad \omega_0^2 = \frac{1}{LC}$$

Also at resonance, $Z_{mot} = R$ [see Fig. 7(c)].

The 'quadrantal frequencies', ω' and ω'' occur when the real and j-parts are equal. Since R is positive, we have,

$$\frac{1}{R} = -\omega'C + \frac{1}{\omega'L} = -\omega'C + \frac{\omega_0^2 C}{\omega'}$$

$$\frac{1}{R} = \omega''C - \frac{1}{\omega''L} = \omega''C - \frac{\omega_0^2 C}{\omega''}$$

Eliminating C in right-hand expressions,

$$-\omega' + \frac{\omega_0^2}{\omega'} = \omega'' - \frac{\omega_0^2}{\omega''}$$

$$(\omega'' + \omega') = \omega_0^2 \left(\frac{1}{\omega'} + \frac{1}{\omega''}\right) = \omega_0^2 \left(\frac{\omega'' + \omega'}{\omega'\omega''}\right)$$

Hence $\omega'\omega'' = \omega_0^2$. Also,

$$\frac{2}{CR} = (\omega'' - \omega') + \omega_0^2 \left(\frac{1}{\omega'} - \frac{1}{\omega''}\right)$$

$$= (\omega'' - \omega') + \omega_0^2 \left(\frac{\omega'' - \omega'}{\omega'\omega''}\right)$$

$$\frac{1}{CR} = (\omega'' - \omega')$$

Using the above relations, values of R, L and C can be determined from measurements at ω_0, ω' and ω'' taken from experimental frequency-response locus.

Now if a small known mass is attached to the moving part a new resonant frequency is measured $= \omega_{0A}$. Then

$$\omega_{0A}^2 = \frac{1}{L(C + \delta C)} \quad \text{and we have} \quad \omega_0^2 = \frac{1}{LC}$$

and

$$\delta C = \left[\frac{\omega_0^2}{\omega_{0A}^2} - 1 \right] C$$

Also $\delta C = \delta M / K_0^2$ so that K_0 is determined.

Then we have (Ref. Ex. 6)

$$M = K_0^2 C; \quad F_v = \frac{K_0^2}{R}; \quad K_s = \frac{K_0^2}{L}$$

Part (b).   From the given data,

$$f' = 196\,\text{Hz}, \quad \text{then} \quad \omega' = 2\pi f' = 1230\,\text{rad/sec}$$

$$f'' = 213\,\text{Hz}, \quad \text{then} \quad \omega'' = 2\pi f'' = 1340\,\text{rad/sec}$$

$$f_0 = 205\,\text{Hz}, \quad \text{then} \quad \omega_0 = 2\pi f_0 = 1290\,\text{rad/sec}$$

$$\text{Diameter of } Z_{\text{mot}} \text{ circle} = 12.15\,\text{ohm} = R$$

Now

$$C = \frac{1}{(\omega'' - \omega')R} = \frac{1}{(1340 - 1230)\,12.15} = \frac{1}{1337}\,\text{farad}$$

$$= 748\,\mu\text{F}$$

$$L = \frac{1}{\omega_0^2 C} = \frac{10^6}{(1290)^2 \times 748} = 0.8 \times 10^{-3}\,\text{henry}$$

For an added mass $= 13\,\text{g}$, $\omega_{0A} = 885\,\text{rad/sec}$ (given)

$$\delta C = C\left[\left(\frac{1290}{885} \right)^2 - 1 \right] = 1.125C$$

$$\frac{\delta C}{C} = \frac{\delta M}{M}$$

$\therefore$

$$M = \frac{13}{1.125} = 11.5\,\text{g}$$

Now we have,

$$K_0^2 = \frac{M}{C} = \frac{11.5 \times 10^{-3}}{748 \times 10^{-6}} = 15.375$$

Then,

$$\text{Spring constant } K_s = \frac{K_0^2}{L} = \frac{15.375}{0.8 \times 10^{-3}}$$

$$= 19.218 \times 10^3 \text{ N/m}$$

$$\text{Viscous friction, } F_v = \frac{K_0^2}{R} = \frac{15.375}{12.15}$$

$$= 1.27 \text{ N sec/m}$$

Example 8

A moving-coil device has inertia J and operates against viscous friction F and spring constraint K_s. The coil is located in a uniform magnetic field of density B. If the system is underdamped, determine an expression for the dynamic movement of the coil element due to (a) application of a constant voltage to the coil, (b) a constant current supply. (c) Obtain an expression for the maximum overshoot of the element in terms of the damping ratio of the system following unit step input.

Solution

The instantaneous forces acting on the coil can be stated,

$$J \frac{d^2\theta}{dt} + F \frac{d\theta}{dt} + K_s\theta = KBi$$

where KBi = instantaneous force due to current i in the coil and K = a constant determined by physical aspects of the coil.

Part (a) & (b). In case (a), with voltage E applied, the instantaneous current in the coil,

$$i = \frac{E - e_g}{R}$$

where $e_g = KB \, d\theta/dt$ and R = ohmic resistance of the coil. Then

$$J \frac{d^2\theta}{dt} + F \frac{d\theta}{dt} + K_s\theta = KB \left(\frac{E - e_g}{R} \right)$$

substituting for e_g and collecting terms in $d\theta/dt$,

$$J\frac{d^2\theta}{dt} + \left(F + \frac{K^2B^2}{R}\right)\frac{d\theta}{dt} + K_s\theta = \frac{KBE}{R} \tag{1}$$

In case (b) with constant current supplied $= I$,

$$J\frac{d^2\theta}{dt} + F\frac{d\theta}{dt} + K_s\theta = KBI \tag{2}$$

In both cases the equations are second order differential equations with constant coefficients. The solution will be the sum of the natural response and the steady-state response.

For the natural response the characteristic equation may be written as (in operational notation),

$$Jp^2 + Dp + K_s = 0$$

where $D =$ damping appropriate to the form of supply.

The roots of this equation are p_1 and p_2 where

$$p_1, p_2 = -\frac{D}{2J} \pm \left(\frac{D^2}{4J^2} - \frac{K_s}{J}\right)^{1/2}$$

This result is expressed in a general notation as,

$$p_1, p_2 = -\alpha \pm j\omega_d$$

where

$$\alpha = \frac{D}{2J} \quad \text{and} \quad \omega_d = \left(\frac{K_s}{J} - \frac{D^2}{4J^2}\right)^{1/2}$$

Then the natural response for the second order system can be expressed,

$$\begin{aligned}
\theta_n &= A_1 \epsilon^{p_1 t} + A_2 \epsilon^{p_2 t} \\
&= A_1 \epsilon^{(-\alpha + j\omega_d)t} + A_2 \epsilon^{(-\alpha - j\omega_d)t} \\
&= \epsilon^{-\alpha t}\{(A_1 + A_2)\cos\omega_d t + j(A_1 - A_2)\sin\omega_d t\} \\
&= A\epsilon^{-\alpha t}\sin(\omega_d t + \phi) \tag{3}
\end{aligned}$$

where

$$A = [(A_1 + A_2)^2 + (A_1 - A_2)^2]^{1/2} \quad \text{and} \quad \phi = \tan^{-1}\frac{(A_1 + A_2)}{(A_1 - A_2)}$$

N.B. In practical terms θ_n is seen as a damped oscillation which decays exponentially, (Fig. 8). This enables α and ω_d to be more fully interpreted, as follows. If there is no damping, $D = 0$ and $\alpha = 0$, and a continuous oscillation occurs.

Then

$$\omega = (K_s/J)^{1/2} = \text{natural angular frequency}$$

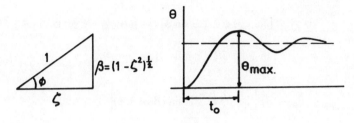

Fig. 8

$$\omega_d = \left(\frac{K_s}{J} - \frac{D^2}{4J^2}\right)^{1/2} = (\omega^2 - \alpha^2)^{1/2}$$

$$= \text{damped angular frequency}$$

A critical value of damping occurs when $D^2/4J^2 = K_s/J$ and $\omega_d = 0$, i.e. no oscillation occurs. Then we have $D_{\text{crit}} = 2(K_s J)^{1/2}$.

A measure of damping is expressed as a damping ratio

$$\zeta = \frac{\text{actual damping}}{\text{critical damping}} = \frac{D}{2(K_s J)^{1/2}} = \frac{\alpha}{\omega}$$

Thus we can interpret $\omega_d = \omega(1 - \zeta^2)^{1/2} = \beta\omega$ where $\beta = (1 - \zeta^2)^{1/2}$.

Note that in this general notation, the characteristic equation. $Jp^2 + Dp + K_s = 0$ can be expressed,

$$p^2 + 2\zeta\omega_n p + \omega_n^2 = 0$$

Now, substituting in equation (3),

$$\theta_n = A\epsilon^{-\zeta\omega t} \sin(\beta\omega t + \phi)$$

Referring to equations (1) and (2), and since steady-state response occurs when $d/dt = 0$,

$$\theta_1 = \frac{KBI}{K_s} \quad [\text{where } I = E/R \text{ for case (a)}]$$

The complete response can be stated, $\theta_0 = \theta_1 + \theta_n$. Thus

$$\theta_0 = \theta_1 + A\epsilon^{-\zeta\omega t} \sin(\beta\omega t + \phi)$$

The constants A and ϕ are evaluated from initial conditions, viz;

$$\frac{d\theta_0}{dt} = A\epsilon^{-\zeta\omega t}(\beta\omega)\cos(\beta\omega t + \phi) + (-\zeta\omega)A\epsilon^{-\zeta\omega t}\sin(\beta\omega t + \phi)$$

If at $t = 0$, $\theta_0 = 0$ and $d\theta_0/dt = 0$, substituting above,

$$0 = \theta_1 + A\sin\phi$$

and

$$0 = A\left[\beta\omega \cos\phi - \zeta\omega \sin\phi\right] = \beta \cos\phi - \zeta \sin\phi$$

Hence

$$\tan\phi = \beta/\zeta \quad \text{and} \quad A = -\frac{1}{\beta}\theta_1$$

Finally,

$$\theta_0 = \theta_1\left[1 - \frac{1}{\beta}e^{-\zeta\omega t}\sin(\beta\omega t + \phi)\right]$$

Part (c).   Overshoot points occur when $d\theta_0/dt = 0$. Working per unit step input

$$\frac{d\theta_0}{dt} = -\frac{1}{\beta}e^{-\zeta\omega t}(\beta\omega)\cos(\beta\omega t + \phi) + \frac{\zeta\omega}{\beta}e^{-\zeta\omega t}\sin(\beta\omega t + \phi)$$

$$= \omega e^{-\zeta\omega t}\left[\frac{\zeta}{\beta}\sin(\beta\omega t + \phi) - \cos(\beta\omega t + \phi)\right]$$

$$= \omega e^{-\zeta\omega t}\left[\frac{\zeta}{\beta}(\sin\beta\omega t\cos\phi + \cos\beta\omega t + \phi)\right.$$
$$\left. - (\cos\beta\omega t\cos\phi - \sin\beta\omega t\sin\phi)\right]$$

Now $\cos\phi = \zeta$, $\sin\phi = \beta$

$$\therefore \quad \frac{d\theta_0}{dt} = \omega e^{-\zeta\omega t}\left[\frac{\zeta^2}{\beta}\sin\beta\omega t + \zeta\cos\beta\omega t - \zeta\cos\beta\omega t + \beta\sin\beta\omega t\right]$$

$$= \omega e^{-\zeta\omega t}\left[\frac{\zeta^2 + \beta^2}{\beta}\right]\sin\beta\omega t$$

$$= \omega e^{-\zeta\omega t}\left(\frac{1}{\beta}\right)\sin\beta\omega t$$

$$= 0 \text{ at overshoot points}$$

Hence the condition at the overshoot points is

$$\sin\beta\omega t = 0$$

The first or maximum overshoot will occur when $\beta\omega t = \pi$. The corresponding instant is $t_0 = \pi/\beta\omega$. At maximum overshoot,

$$\theta_{max} = 1 - \frac{1}{\beta}e^{-\zeta\omega t}\sin(\beta\omega t + \phi)$$

$$= 1 - \frac{1}{\beta}e^{-\pi\zeta/\beta}(\sin\pi\cos\phi + \cos\pi\sin\phi)$$

$$= (1 + e^{-\pi\zeta/\beta})$$

$\therefore$ First overshoot $= \epsilon^{-\pi\zeta/\beta}$ per unit step input

In terms of the given-system constants

$$\frac{\zeta}{\beta} = \alpha/(\omega^2 - \alpha^2)^{1/2} = \frac{\alpha}{\omega_d}$$

$$= \frac{D}{(4K_sJ - D^2)^{1/2}}$$

Example 9

An induction-disc overcurrent relay has a characteristic as shown in Fig. 9(a). The relay is supplied by a 100/1 A current transformer on a 3-phase 11 kV local feeder of reactance 3 ohm/phase. The feeder is supplied by an 80 MVA 33/11 kV transformer of 0.1 p.u. reactance which, in turn, is fed by a 33 kV line of 6 ohm reactance. This line is fed by a 100 MVA 132/33 kV transformer of 0.1 p.u. reactance connected to a 132 kV supply by a line of 13 ohm reactance. It is required to calculate the fault current and the time of operation of the relay, due to a 3-phase solid earth fault on the 11 kV feeder, given that the relay has a plug setting multiplier, (P.S.M.) of 125% and a time multiplier, (T.M.) of 0.6.

Solution

The arrangement of the system may be drawn as shown in Figure 9(b).

For computational purposes given values of reactances are referred to a convenient common base MVA. In general, if I and V are rated or base reference values, then

$$Z_{pu} = \frac{IZ}{V} \quad \text{where } Z \text{ is in ohm units and pu means 'per unit'}$$

Hence,

$$Z_{ohm} = \frac{V}{I}(Z_{pu}) = \frac{V^2}{VI}(Z_{pu}) = \frac{(V_{base})^2}{(VA_{base})}(Z_{pu})$$

Also

$$Z_{pu} = (Z_{ohm})\frac{(VA_{base})}{(V_{base})^2}$$

The rated voltage is the base voltage for a given section.

Adopting

$$S_{base} = \frac{100}{3} \text{ MVA} \quad \text{in this calculation}$$

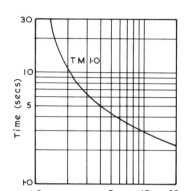

(a)

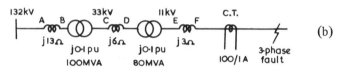

(b)

Fig. 9

$$X_{AB} = 13 \times \frac{100}{3} \times \frac{1}{(132/\sqrt{3})^2} = 0.0746 \, \text{pu}$$

$$X_{BC} = 0.1 \, \text{pu (already on the correct per unit base)}$$

$$X_{CD} = 6 \times \frac{100}{3} \times \frac{1}{(33/\sqrt{3})^2} = 0.55 \, \text{pu}$$

$$X_{DE} = 0.1 \times \frac{100}{80} = 0.125 \, \text{pu}$$

$$X_{EF} = 3 \times \frac{100}{3} \times \frac{1}{(11/\sqrt{3})^2} = 2.48 \, \text{pu}$$

$$\text{Total } jX = j \sum X = j3.33 \, \text{pu}$$

$$\text{Per Unit fault current} = \frac{1.0 + j0}{j3.33} = -j0.3 \, \text{pu}$$

Now

$$\text{Base current on 11 kV} = \frac{\text{base MVA}}{(11/\sqrt{3}) \, \text{kV}} = \frac{100 \times 10^6}{3} \times \frac{\sqrt{3}}{11 \times 10^3}$$

$$= 5249 \, \text{A}$$

$$\text{Fault current} = 0.3 \times 5249 = 1576 \text{ A}$$

With a C.T. of 100/1 A, relay coil current $= 1576/100 = 15.76$ A.
With plug setting of 125%, effective relay current $= 12.6$ A.
From graph, (Fig. 9(a)) with T.M. $= 1.0$,

$$\text{Relay time} = 2.65 \text{ sec}$$

$$\text{Actual relay time, (with T.M.} = 0.6), = 2.65 \times 0.6$$

$$= 1.59 \text{ sec}$$

Example 10

Each conductor of a 3-phase 66 kV transmission line with the neutral solidly earthed, is supported by an insulator string of six units. Each unit has a self capacitance of 60 picofarad and a capacitance from cap-pin coupling to earth of 6 picofarad. It is required to calculate the voltage across the unit subjected to highest electrical stress, and the 'string efficiency'.

Solution

The equivalent circuit of the arrangement can be represented as in Fig. 10. Because the neutral is earthed, the total voltage across the string is $V_p = V_L/\sqrt{3} = 38\,100$ volt.

Leakage current from the line through the string is maximum in Unit 1, (next to the line), and is progressively reduced by leakage to earth via cap-pin capacitance to earth. Thus maximum voltage will occur across Unit 1. We can define

$$k = \frac{\text{cap to earth capacitance}}{\text{unit self capacitance}} = \frac{6}{60} = 0.1$$

A step-by-step analysis gives:

$$I_6 = j\omega C V_6 \quad \text{and} \quad I_{E5} = j\omega k C V_6$$

$$I_5 = I_6 + I_{E5} = j\omega C V_6 (1 + k) = j\omega C V_6 (1.1)$$

$$V_5 = \frac{I_5}{j\omega C} = (1.1) V_6$$

$$I_{E4} = j(V_6 + V_5)\omega k C = j(1 + 1.1)\omega k C V_6 = (0.21) j\omega C V_6$$

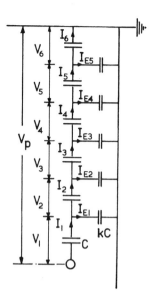

Fig. 10

$$I_4 = I_5 + I_{E4} = j\omega C V_6(1.1 + 0.21) = (1.31)j\omega C V_6$$

$$V_4 = \frac{I_4}{j\omega C} = (1.31)V_6$$

$$I_{E3} = j(V_6 + V_5 + V_4)\omega k C = jV_6(1 + 1.1 + 1.31)(0.1)\omega C$$
$$= (0.341)j\omega C V_6$$

$$I_3 = I_4 + I_{E3} = (1.31 + 0.341)j\omega C V_6 = (1.651)j\omega C V_6$$

$$V_3 = \frac{I_3}{j\omega C} = (1.651)V_6$$

$$I_{E2} = j(V_6 + V_5 + V_4 + V_3)\omega k C$$
$$= jV_6(1 + 1.1 + 1.31 + 1.651)(0.1)\omega C = (0.506)j\omega C V_6$$

$$I_2 = I_3 + I_{E2} = (0.506 + 1.651)j\omega C V_6 = (2.157)j\omega C V_6$$

$$V_2 = \frac{I_2}{j\omega C} = (2.157)V_6$$

$$I_{E1} = j(V_6 + V_5 + V_4 + V_3 + V_2)\omega k C$$
$$= j(1 + 1.1 + 1.31 + 1.651 + 2.157)(0.1)\omega C V_6$$
$$= (0.722)j\omega C V_6$$

$$I_1 = I_2 + I_{E1} = (2.157 + 0.722)j\omega C V_6 = (2.879)j\omega C V_6$$

$$V_1 = \frac{I_1}{j\omega C} = (2.879)V_6$$

Now

$$V_p = \sum V_n = 10.096 V_6 = 38\,100 \text{ volt}$$

$$V_6 = \frac{38\,100}{10.096} = 3773 \text{ volt}$$

Hence

$$V_1 = 2.879 V_6 = 2.879 \times 3773 = 10\,860 \text{ volt}$$

$$\text{String efficiency} = \frac{\text{voltage over string}}{\text{No. of units} \times \text{highest unit voltage}}$$

$$= \frac{38\,100}{6 \times 10\,860} = 0.585$$

Alternatively; for a limited enquiry and where there are many units (n), we can express the voltage to earth at the mth unit, (counting from the line), using hyperbolic functions, (Ref. 12, p. 135)

$$V_{Em} = V\left[\frac{\sinh{(n-m)}\sqrt{k}}{\sinh{(n\sqrt{k})}}\right]$$

Thus

$$V_{E1} = V_p\left[\frac{\sinh{(6-1)}\sqrt{0.1}}{\sinh{(6\sqrt{0.1})}}\right] = 38\,100\left(\frac{\sinh 1.581}{\sinh 1.897}\right)$$

$$= 38\,100 \times \frac{2.32}{3.25} = 27\,240 \text{ volt} \quad \text{to earth}$$

Then

$$\text{volts across unit } 1 = V_p - V_{E1} = 38\,100 - 27\,240$$

$$= 10\,860 \text{ volt} \quad \text{(as before)}$$

N.B. In practice pollution of the surfaces of the insulating units results in an effective shunt resistance path across each unit self-capacitance. The effect is to give a more uniform voltage distribution over the string.

Example 11

A circuit breaker disconnects a predominantly capacitative load from an a.c. supply, of source inductance L, at the zero of the a.c. cycle. If a restrike occurs one third of a cycle after the interruption, show that the maximum value of the transient voltage across the load is twice the peak of the supply a.c. voltage. Comment on critical conditions.

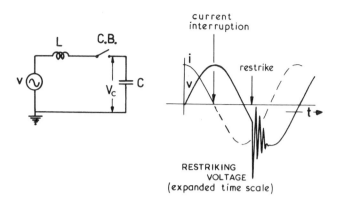

Fig. 11

Solution (Ref. 7. p. 376)

Fig. 11 illustrates the condition.

At interruption $i = 0$ and the capacitor is left charged to V_m. Restrike occurs $\frac{1}{3}$ cycle later.

∴   Voltage across breaker gap at restrike $= V_m + V_m \sin 30°$

$$= \tfrac{3}{2} V_m$$

At restrike,

$$L \, di/dt + \frac{1}{C} \int i \, dt = \frac{3V_m}{2}$$

The characteristic equation can be written,

$$p^2 + \frac{1}{LC} = 0 \quad \text{where} \quad p = \frac{d}{dt}$$

∴ $$p = \pm \sqrt{\left(-\frac{1}{LC}\right)} = \pm j\omega_0$$

where ω_0 = natural angular frequency of circuit $= \sqrt{(1/LC)}$.

Instantaneous current at restrike,

$$i = A \cos \omega_0 t + jB \sin \omega_0 t$$

At $t = 0, i = 0$. Hence $A = 0$ and $i = jB \sin \omega_0 t$. Then

$$L \, di/dt = j\omega_0 LB \cos \omega_0 t$$

At $t = 0$,

$$j\omega_0 LB = 3V_m/2$$

$$\therefore \qquad B = \frac{3V_m}{2j\omega_0 L}$$

$$i = \frac{3V_m}{2\omega_0 L} \sin \omega_0 t$$

Now,

$$V_c = V_m - \frac{1}{C}\int i\,dt = V_m - \frac{1}{C}\frac{3V_m}{2\omega_0 L}\int_0^t \sin \omega_0 t\,dt$$

$$= V_m + \frac{3V_m}{2\omega_0^2 LC}[\cos \omega_0 t]_0^t$$

$$= V_m + \frac{3V_m}{2}[\cos \omega_0 t]_0^t$$

This is maximum negative when $\cos \omega_0 t = -1$. Then

$$V_c = V_m - \tfrac{3}{2}V_m - \tfrac{3}{2}V_m = -2V_m$$

Comment. With a restrike occurring $\frac{1}{2}$ cycle after the current interruption we obtain $V_c = -3V_m$, which is also the potential of the circuit breaker contact relative to earth. In practice circuit resistance would reduce these maximum values.

Attenuation of the recovery voltage transient is obtained by connecting resistance across the circuit breaker contacts. Critical damping occurs when $R = \frac{1}{2}\sqrt{(L/C)}$ and transient attenuation occurs exponentially as $e^{-\alpha t}$ where $\alpha = R/2L$. Added resistance also raises the power factor, so that the supply voltage is then not at peak value at the interruption of the circuit current.

Example 12

A Peterson coil of inductance L is connected between earth and the neutral point of a 3 phase 33 kV 50 Hz transmission system to minimise the fault current, due to an earth fault on one line. The sound lines each has capacitance to earth $C = 2.5\ \mu F$. It is required to determine a suitable value for L and the current rating of the coil.

Solution

The circuit arrangement and the phasor diagram may be shown as in Fig. 12.
    The currents are

$$I_R = \frac{V_{RB}}{X_c} \quad \text{leading } V_{RB} \text{ by } 90°$$

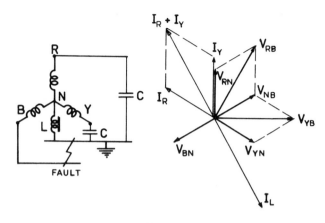

Fig. 12

$$I_Y = \frac{V_{YB}}{X_c} \quad \text{leading } V_{YB} \text{ by } 90°$$

I_L, in the Peterson coil, $= \dfrac{V_{NB}}{X_L}$ lagging V_{NB} by $90°$

The resultant fault current to earth is zero when,

$$\mathbf{I_L} = \mathbf{I_R} + \mathbf{I_Y} = \frac{\mathbf{V_{RB}} + \mathbf{V_{YB}}}{X_c}$$

$$= \frac{\sqrt{3}V_{RB}}{X_c} = \frac{V_{NB}}{X_L}$$

Now, $V_{RB} = \sqrt{3}V_{NB}$. Hence

Then

$$\frac{\sqrt{3} \times \sqrt{3}}{X_c} = \frac{1}{X_L}$$

$$X_L = \frac{X_c}{3} \quad \text{or} \quad \omega L = \frac{1}{3\omega C}$$

$$L = \frac{1}{3\omega^2 C}$$

For the given data

$$L = \frac{1}{3\omega^2 C} = \frac{10^6}{3(2\pi \times 50)^2 \times 2.5}$$

$$= 1.3 \text{ henry}$$

$$I_L = \frac{V_{NB}}{X_L} = \frac{33 \times 10^3}{\sqrt{3}} \times \frac{1}{(2\pi \times 50) \times 1.3}$$

$$= 46.67 \text{ amp}$$

N.B.   The Peterson coil is popular for grounding transformer neutrals, below 70 kV, (Ref. 16, p. 156), in U.S.A. and Europe, though not common practice in Britain.

Example 13

A graphite moderated enriched uranium power reactor generates 1000 MW of thermal power. It is required to calculate the weight of U^{235} burnt per day. The following data are given; each fission releases 200 MeV energy; charge on an electron = 1.6×10^{-19} coulomb; Avogadro's number = 6×10^{23} atoms/gm atom.

Solution

$$\text{Charge on one electron} = 1.6 \times 10^{-19} \text{ coulomb}$$

$$1 \text{ eV} = 1.6 \times 10^{-19} \text{ joules}$$

$$1 \text{ MeV} = 1.6 \times 10^{-13} \text{ joules}$$

$$\therefore \quad 1 \text{ watt} = 1 \text{ joule/sec} = \frac{10^{13}}{1.6} \text{ MeV/sec} = 6.25 \times 10^{12} \text{ MeV/sec}$$

$$= \frac{6.25 \times 10^{12}}{200} = 3.1 \times 10^{10} \text{ fissions/sec}$$

$$1 \text{ gram, Uranium 235,} = \frac{\text{Avogadro's number}}{235} = \frac{6 \times 10^{23}}{235}$$

$$= 2.55 \times 10^{21} \text{ atoms.}$$

$$1 \text{ watt/day, fissions,} = 3.1 \times 10^{10} \times 24 \times 3600$$

$$= 2.68 \times 10^{15} \text{ atoms } U^{235}/\text{day}$$

$$\therefore \quad 1 \text{ watt} = \frac{2.68 \times 10^{15}}{2.55 \times 10^{21}} = 1.05 \times 10^{-6} \text{ gm/day}$$

$$\therefore \quad \text{Weight of uranium/day, for 1000 MW power}$$

$$= 1.05 \text{ kg/day}$$

Chapter Two

Transformers

Example 14

A 60 Hz transformer has copper, hysteresis and eddy current losses of 2%, 1.2% and 0.7% respectively. Determine the percentage loss in each case when the transformer is operated on a 50 Hz supply of the same voltage and with the same load current. How should the rating of the transformer be modified to give the same temperature rise? Assume Steinmetz index is 1.6.

Solution (Ref. 2, p. 269).

For a transformer, $V = 4.44\Phi_m fT$ volt. Hence, for constant V, $\Phi_m \propto 1/f$.

$$\therefore \quad \text{New } \Phi_m = \frac{60}{50}\Phi_m \quad \text{and} \quad \text{new } B_m = B_{m1} = \frac{60}{50}B_m$$

$$\text{Hysteresis loss} = k_h B_m^{1.6} f = 1.2\%$$

$$\text{New hysteresis loss} = k_h B_{m1}^{1.6} f_1 = (k_h B_m^{1.6} f)\left(\frac{B_{m1}}{B_m}\right)^{1.6}\left(\frac{f_1}{f}\right)$$

$$= 1.2 \times \left(\frac{60}{50}\right)^{1.6}\left(\frac{50}{60}\right) = 1.2 \times 1.115$$

$$= 1.338\%$$

$$\text{Eddy current loss} = k_e B_m^2 f^2 = 0.7\% \quad \text{(given)}$$

$$\text{New eddy current loss} = k_e B_{m1}^2 f_1^2 = 0.7 \times \left(\frac{B_{m1}}{B_m}\right)^2\left(\frac{f_1}{f}\right)^2 .$$

$$= 0.7 \times \left(\frac{60}{50}\right)^2\left(\frac{50}{60}\right)^2 = 0.7\%$$

$$\text{Copper loss} = I^2 R = 2\% \quad \text{(unchanged)}$$

For unchanged temperature rise, total losses will be unchanged. Hence copper losses must be reduced by $(1.338 - 1.2) = 0.138\%$, to allow for increase in hysteresis loss, i.e.

New copper loss required $= 1.862\%$

$$\text{Ratio of copper losses, new/old} = \frac{1.862}{2} = 0.931$$

$$\text{Ratio of currents} = (0.931)^{1/2} = 0.965$$

$\therefore$ New rating $= 96.5\%$ of original rating

Example 15

Two identical 6.4 kVA, 240/640 V single-phase transformers are tested by the Sumpner 'back-to-back' method. On 240 V supply mains, the wattmeters in the primary and secondary circuits indicate 192 W and 240 W respectively, under full-load conditions. Calculate:

(a) the efficiency of one of the transformers when supplying a load of 3 kW, 0.8 lagging p.f.,

(b) the secondary current for maximum efficiency.

Solution (Fig. 15)

In this test the primary supply wattmeter indicates the combined no load losses for the transformers and the secondary wattmeter gives the combined copper losses.

Hence, for one transformer,

$$W_0 = \frac{192}{2} = 96 \text{ W}$$

$$\text{Full-load } W_{cu} = \frac{240}{2} = 120 \text{ W}$$

$$\text{Rated full-load secondary current, } I_2(FL) = \frac{6.4 \times 10^3}{640}$$

$$= 10 \text{ A}$$

$\therefore$ Total equivalent resistance, referred to the secondary

$$R'' = \frac{W_{cu}}{I_2^2} = \frac{120}{100} = 1.2 \text{ ohm}$$

Part (a).   For a load of 3 kW, 0.8 p.f., at 640 volt.

$$I_2 = \frac{3000}{640 \times 0.8} = 5.85 \text{ amp}$$

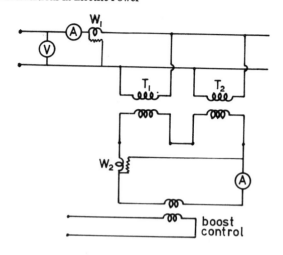

Fig. 15

Copper loss at this load $= I_2^2 R'' = (5.85)^2 \times 1.2 = 41$ watt

$$\therefore \qquad \text{Efficiency} = \frac{\text{output}}{\text{output} + \text{losses}}$$

$$\eta = \frac{3000}{3000 + 41 + 96} = \frac{3000}{3137}$$

$$= 95.6\%$$

Part (b).   At maximum efficiency, copper losses = core losses, i.e.

Then
$$W_{cu} = W_0 = 96\,\text{W} = I_2^2 R''$$

$$I_2^2 = \frac{96}{1.2} = 80$$

Hence
$$I_2(\text{max } \eta) = 8.95 \text{ A}$$

Example 16

A given oil-immersed power transformer, operating on full load, has a temperature rise of $15°C$ after 1 hour and $26.68°C$ after 2 hours. The transformer has a full-load copper loss equal to twice the core loss and the temperature-rise of the oil is proportional to the losses dissipated. Calculate:

    (a) the thermal time constant,
    (b) the final steady temperature rise on full load,
    (c) the permissible 1 hour rating for the same temperature rise.

Solution (Ref. 7, p. 313; Ref. 6, p. 120).

The temperature rises exponentially with time, and the rise can be expressed

$$\theta = \theta_m(1 - e^{-t/T})$$

where θ_m = final steady temperature rise, and T = thermal time constant in hours.

(a) Substituting numerical values, we have,

$$15 = \theta_m(1 - e^{-t/T}) = \theta_m(1 - e^{-1/T})$$

$$26.68 = \theta_m(1 - e^{-2/T})$$

Hence,

$$\frac{(1 - e^{-2/T})}{(1 - e^{-1/T})} = (1 + e^{-1/T}) = \frac{26.68}{15} = 1.7787$$

$\therefore$

$$e^{-1/T} = 0.7787$$

$$-1/T = \ln 0.7787 = -0.25$$

Thermal time constant, $T = 4$ hours.

(b) Substituting again,

$$15 = \theta_m(1 - 0.7787) = \theta_m(0.2213)$$

$\therefore$

$$\theta_m = \frac{15}{0.2213} = 67.78°C \text{ rise.}$$

(c) On overload for 1 hour, $\theta = 67.78$. Then

$$\theta = 67.78 = \theta_{m_1}(1 - e^{-1/T})$$

$$= 0.2213\theta_{m_1}$$

The ratio

$$\theta_{m_1}/\theta = 1/0.2213 = \frac{\text{losses on 1 hour rating}}{\text{losses on full load}}$$

At K times full-load rating,

$$\text{Copper loss} = K^2(\text{full-load copper loss})$$

$$= 2K^2(\text{core loss})$$

Then

$$\text{the ratio} = \frac{(2K^2 + 1)(\text{core loss})}{(2 + 1)(\text{core loss})} = \frac{2K^2 + 1}{3}$$

$$= \frac{1}{0.2213}$$

$$K^2 = 6.278$$

$$K = 2.5 \text{ times full-load rating}$$

Example 17

Open-circuit and short-circuit tests are carried out on a 3-phase 20 kVA Δ/Y, 415/183 volt, power transformer. The test results are given: O.C. test, with meters on the L.V. side and normal 183 volts applied, total $W_{OC} = 240$ watt, $I_L = 7.1$ amp; S.C. test with input to the H.V. side, the H.V. winding being connected in Y, total $W_{sc} = 405$ watt, $I_L = 16.1$ amp and $V_L = 23.8$ volt. Calculate:

(a) the equivalent circuit referred to the H.V. side,
(b) the full-load efficiency with loads at (i) power factor unity, (ii) power factor 0.8 lagging,
(c) percentage of full load for maximum efficiency.

Solution

Part (a).   Working PER PHASE.
From the O.C. test results,

$$W_0 = \frac{240}{3} = 80 \text{ watt/phase}$$

$$I_0 = 7.1 \text{ amp}$$

$$V_0 = \frac{183}{\sqrt{3}} = 105.7 \text{ volt}$$

Then

$$\cos\phi_0 = \frac{W_0}{V_0 I_0} = \frac{80}{105.7 \times 7.1} = 0.107$$

The energy component of

$$I_0 = I_e = I_0 \cos\phi_0$$

$$= 7.1 \times 0.107 = 0.76 \text{ amp}$$

The magnetising component of

$$I_0 = I_m = I_0 \sin\phi_0$$

$$= 7.1 \times 0.994 = 7.057 \text{ amp}$$

Then

$$R_0'' = \frac{V_0}{I_e} = \frac{105.7}{0.76} = 139.08 \text{ ohm/phase}$$

$$X_0'' = \frac{V_0}{I_m} = \frac{105.7}{7.057} = 14.97 \text{ ohm/phase}$$

Referring these values to the H.V. winding, (see **N.B.** below),

$$R_0' = k^2 R_0'' = \left(\frac{415}{105.7}\right)^2 \times 139.08 = 2143.9 \text{ ohm/phase}$$

$$X_0' = k^2 X_0'' = \left(\frac{415}{105.7}\right)^2 \times 14.97 = 230.8 \text{ ohm/phase}$$

From the S.C. test results,

$$W_{sc} = \frac{405}{3} = 135 \text{ watt/phase}$$

$$I_{sc} = 16.1 \text{ amp} \quad \text{and} \quad V_{sc} = \frac{23.8}{\sqrt{3}} = 13.74 \text{ volt}$$

Then

$$Z_{sc}' = \frac{V_{sc}}{I_{sc}} = \frac{13.74}{16.1} = 0.853 \text{ ohm/phase}$$

$$R' = \frac{W_{sc}}{I_{sc}^2} = \frac{135}{(16.1)^2} = 0.521 \text{ ohm/phase}$$

$$X' = (Z_{sc}^2 - R'^2)^{1/2} = (0.456)^{1/2} = 0.675 \text{ ohm/phase}$$

Part (b).   On rated full load,

$$I_L = \frac{20\,000}{\sqrt{3} \times 415} = 27.8 \text{ amp}$$

$$I_{ph} = \frac{27.8}{\sqrt{3}} = 16.1 \text{ amp}$$

Hence full-load copper losses = 405 watt (since $I_{sc} = I_{FL}$). At unity p.f.,

$$\text{Full-load efficiency} = \frac{\text{output}}{\text{output} + \text{losses}}$$

$$= \frac{20\,000}{20\,000 + 405 + 240} = 0.969 \quad \text{or } 96.9\%$$

At 0.8 p.f.,

$$\text{efficiency} = \frac{\sqrt{3}VI \cos\phi}{\sqrt{3}VI \cos\phi + 3I^2R + W_0}$$

$$= \frac{16\,000}{16\,000 + 405 + 240} = 0.961 \quad \text{or } 96.1\%$$

Part (c).   The condition for maximum efficiency is $I^2R = W_0$. Hence

$$I^2R = 80 \text{ watt/ph}$$

$$I^2 = \frac{80}{0.521} = 153.55$$

$$\therefore \qquad I = (153.55)^{1/2} = 12.4 \text{ A/ph}$$

$$I_L = \sqrt{3} \times 12.4 = 21.48 \text{ amp}$$

$$\therefore \qquad \% \text{ Full load} = \frac{21.48}{27.8} \times 100 = 77.27\%$$

N.B.   Equivalent circuit for one-line diagram analyses (Ref. 16, p. 159).

Working phase to phase, referred impedance values are obtained, traditionally, by multiplying by the square of the turns ratio. In one-line representation line voltages are used to represent the ratio. For $Y-Y$ connections no change is required, but for $\Delta-Y$ the necessary multiplying factor becomes $(V_{L1}/V_{L2})^2 = (T_1/\sqrt{3}T_2)^2$.

In effect the $\Delta-Y$ is being assumed to be replaced by $Y-Y$ giving the required line/line voltage transformation. In this example we would get, $R_0' = 714.63$ ohm and $X_0' = 76.92$ ohm.

Example 18

Two single-phase 100 kVA transformers of the same turns-ratio share a load of 150 kVA, 0.8 power factor lagging. Transformer A has resistance and reactance drops of 4% and 7% respectively. The corresponding figures for transformer B are 1.5% and 5%. Calculate the kVA loading and power factor of each transformer.

Solution (Ref. 2, p. 276).

Parallel operation imposes equal voltage regulation, i.e.

$$I_A Z_A = I_B Z_B = I\left(\frac{Z_A Z_B}{Z_A + Z_B}\right)$$

whence

$$I_A = I\left(\frac{Z_B}{Z_A + Z_B}\right) \quad \text{and} \quad I_B = I\left(\frac{Z_A}{Z_A + Z_B}\right)$$

At common terminal voltage V,

$$VI_A = VI\left(\frac{Z_B}{Z_A + Z_B}\right) \quad \text{or} \quad S_A = S\left(\frac{Z_B}{Z_A + Z_B}\right)$$

and

$$S_B = S\left(\frac{Z_A}{Z_A + Z_B}\right)$$

where $S = (kW \pm j\,kVAR) = kVA\underline{/\pm\phi}$ and all quantities are in vector notation.

Numerical part.   Combined load $S = 150\underline{/-36.9°} = (120 - j90)\,kVA$.

$$Z_A\% = (4 + j7) = (65)^{1/2}\underline{/\tan^{-1}7/4} = 8.06\underline{/60.2°}$$

$$Z_B\% = (1.5 + j5) = (27.25)^{1/2}\underline{/\tan^{-1}5/1.5} = 5.22\underline{/73.3°}$$

$$Z_A\% + Z_B\% = (5.5 + j12) = (174.25)^{1/2}\underline{/\tan^{-1}12/5.5} = 13.2\underline{/65.3°}$$

$$S_A = \frac{150 \times 5.22}{13.2}\underline{/-36.9 + 73.3 - 65.3}$$

$$= 59.3\underline{/-28.9°}\ kVA$$

$$= 52\,kW\ @\ p.f.\ 0.875\ lagging.$$

$$S_B = \frac{150 \times 8.06}{13.2}\underline{/-36.9 + 60.2 - 65.3}$$

$$= 91.6\underline{/-42°}\ kVA$$

$$= 68\,kW\ @\ p.f.\ 0.743\ lagging.$$

Notes.   (a) As a check, note that the kW add arithmetically, but the KVA add as phasors.

(2) It was permissible to use $Z\%$ in place of ohmic Z since the nominal rating, (i.e. base) is the same for both transformers and $Z\% = (IZ/V) \times 100$ where V and I are rated values. Example 19 demonstrates the adjustment required where the ratings are not the same.

(3) Higher inherent accuracy is obtained if angles are expressed in degrees and minutes. This is also demonstrated in Ex. 19. In the present example we have:

$$Z_A\% = 8.06\underline{/60°15'}$$

$$Z_B\% = 5.22\underline{/73°18'}$$

$$Z_A\% + Z_B\% = 13.2\underline{/65°22'}$$

The subsequent solution agrees with the solution given before, in this case.

Example 19

A 600 kVA star/star 3-phase transformer, with percentage impedance of $(1.2 + j4.0)$/phase, is paralleled with a 900 kVA star/star transformer with a percentage impedance $(0.6 + j9.0)$/phase. Calculate the kVA load of each transformer and its power factor, when they share a load of 1000 kW, 0.8 power factor lagging. The transformers have the same turns ratio.

Solution

$$\text{Common load} = \frac{1000}{0.8} = 1250 \text{ kVA at } \phi = -36.9°$$

$$S_A = S\left(\frac{Z_B}{Z_A + Z_B}\right) \quad \text{and} \quad S_B = S\left(\frac{Z_A}{Z_A + Z_B}\right)$$

in symbolic notation (Ref. 2, p. 276), where Z_A and Z_B are in ohm units.

Now $Z\% = (IZ \times 100)/V$ where V and I are rated values. Then $Z\%$ may be used in place of ohmic Z providing the base, (i.e. nominal rating) is the same for both transformers. In this case take a common base of 900 kVA. Then

$$\text{adjusted } Z_A\% = \frac{9}{6}(1.2 + j4) = (1.8 + j6)$$

$$= (39.24)^{1/2}/\tan^{-1} 6/1.8 = 6.26 \underline{/73.3°}$$

$$Z_B\% = (0.6 + j9) = (81.36)^{1/2}/\tan^{-1} 9/0.6 = 9.02 \underline{/86.2°}$$

$$Z_A\% + Z_B\% = (2.4 + j15) = (230.76)^{1/2}/\tan^{-1} 15/2.4$$

$$= 15.2 \underline{/-80.9°}$$

Then,

$$S_A = \frac{1250 \times 9.02|}{15.2} \underline{/-36.9 + 86.2 - 80.9}$$

$$= 742 \underline{/-31.6°} \text{ kVA and } \cos \phi_A = 0.85 \text{ lagging}$$

$$S_B = \frac{1250 \times 6.26}{15.2} \underline{/-36.9 + 73.3 - 80.9}$$

$$= 515 \underline{/-44.5°} \text{ kVA} \quad \text{and} \quad \cos \phi_B = 0.713 \text{ lagging}$$

Check (1)

$$kW_A + kW_B = 742 \times 0.85 + 515 \times 0.713$$

$$= 632 + 367 = 999 \text{ kW}$$

(2) Using the higher accuracy of minutes for subdivision of angles, and logarithms;

$$Z_A\% = 6.26 \underline{/73°18'}$$

$$Z_B\% = 9.02 \underline{/86°12'}$$

$$Z_A\% + Z_B\% = 15.19 \underline{/80°54'}$$

Then

$$S_A = 742.2 \underline{/-31°34'} \quad \text{and} \quad \cos \phi_A = 0.852 \text{ lagging}$$

$$S_B = 515.1 \underline{/-44°28'} \quad \text{and} \quad \cos \phi_B = 0.713 \text{ lagging}$$

This checks as follows

$$\log 515.1 = 2.7119$$

$$\log \cos 44°28' = \overline{1}.8535$$

$$2.5654 \quad \therefore \quad kW_B = 367.6$$

$$\log 742.2 = 2.8705$$

$$\log \cos 31°34' = \overline{1}.9305$$

$$2.8010 \quad \therefore \quad kW_A = 632.4$$

$$\text{Total kW} = 1000.0$$

Example 20

Two single phase transformers are operating in parallel on both primary and secondary sides. Transformer A has a rating of 1000 kVA, open-circuit secondary voltage of 520 V and full-load resistance and reactance drops of 1% and 4% respectively. The corresponding figures for transformer B are 600 kVA, 510 V, 0.8% and 5%. Find the secondary currents and power factors when the transformers share a load of 1200 kVA, power factor 0.9 lagging. Assume the loaded output voltage is 500 V.

Solution

The current delivered by transformer A,

$$I_A = \frac{E_A Z_B + (E_A - E_B)Z}{Z_A Z_B + Z(Z_A + Z_B)}$$

and by transformer B, a similar expression with A and B transposed (Ref. 2, p. 276).

The specification can be expressed,

$$I_A R_A = 1\% \text{ of } 500 \text{ V} = 5 \text{ V} \quad \therefore R_A = \frac{5}{2000} = 0.0025 \text{ ohm}$$

$$I_A X_A = 4\% \text{ of } 500 \text{ V} = 20 \text{ V} \quad \therefore X_A = \frac{20}{2000} = 0.01 \text{ ohm}$$

$$I_B R_B = 0.8\% \text{ of } 500\,\text{V} = 4\,\text{V} \quad \therefore R_B = \frac{4}{1200} = 0.0033 \text{ ohm}$$

$$I_B X_B = 5\% \text{ of } 500\,\text{V} = 25\,\text{V} \quad \therefore X_B = \frac{25}{1200} = 0.020\,83 \text{ ohm}$$

Then

$$Z_A = 0.0025 + j0.01 = 0.0103\,\underline{/75°58'}$$

$$Z_B = 0.0033 + j0.0208 = 0.021\,07\,\underline{/80°54'}$$

$$Z_A + Z_B = 0.0058 + j0.0308 = 0.031\,34\,\underline{/79°17'}$$

The common load,

Hence

$$S = 1200\,\underline{/-25°50'} = (V^2/Z) \times 10^{-3}\,\text{kVA}$$

$$\text{load } Z = \frac{(500)^2}{10^3 \times 1200\,\underline{/-25°50'}} = 0.2083\,\underline{/25°50'}$$

$$= 0.1875 + j0.090\,76$$

Substituting in the expression for I_A,

$$I_A =$$

$$\frac{520(0.0033 + j0.0208) + 10(0.1875 + j0.090\,76)}{(0.0103\,\underline{/75°58'})(0.021\,07\,\underline{/80°54'}) + (0.2083\,\underline{/25°50'})(0.031\,34\,\underline{/79°17'})}$$

$$= \frac{1.716 + j10.82 + 1.875 + j0.9076}{2.17 \times 10^{-4}\,\underline{/156°52'} + 65.28 \times 10^{-4}\,\underline{/105°7'}}$$

$$= \frac{3.591 + j11.73}{(-1.995 + j0.8525 - 17.02 + j63.01) \times 10^{-4}}$$

$$= \frac{3.591 + j11.73}{(-19.02 + j63.86) \times 10^{-4}} = \frac{12.27\,\underline{/72°59'}}{66.88 \times 10^{-4}\,\underline{/106°35'}}$$

$$= 1835\,\underline{/-33°36'}$$

∴

$$I_A = 1835 \text{ amps @ } \cos\phi = 0.833 \text{ lagging}$$

$$I_B = \frac{510(0.0025 + j0.01) - 10(0.1875 + j0.090\,76)}{66.88 \times 10^{-4}\,\underline{/106°35'}}$$

$$= \frac{-0.6 + j4.192}{66.88 \times 10^{-4}\,\underline{/106°35'}} = \frac{4.235\,\underline{/98°8'}}{66.88 \times 10^{-4}\,\underline{/106°35'}}$$

$$= 633.2\,\underline{/-8°27'}$$

∴

$$I_B = 633.2 \text{ amps @ } \cos\phi = 0.989 \text{ lagging}$$

Chapter Three
D.C. Machines

Example 21

A 240 V d.c. shunt motor takes a line current of 22 amps when running on load at 500 rpm. The armature and field resistances are 0.5 ohm and 120 ohm respectively. Assuming constant load torque, calculate:

(a) the added field resistance necessary to increase the speed to 1000 rpm,
(b) the speed to give maximum output.

Solution (Ref. 2, p. 114; Ref. 3, p. 260).

Part (a). For a d.c. machine, $T \propto \Phi I_a \propto I_f I_a =$ constant, (given).

$\therefore \qquad\qquad I_{a1}/I_{a2} = I_{f2}/I_{f1}$

Also,
$$E_b = K\Phi N \propto I_f N$$

$\therefore \qquad\qquad \dfrac{E_{b1}}{E_{b2}} = \dfrac{I_{f1}N_1}{I_{f2}N_2}$

At 500 rpm,
$$I_{f1} = \frac{V}{R_f} = \frac{240}{120} = 2 \text{ amp}$$

$$I_{a1} = 22 - 2 = 20 \text{ amp}$$

Then
$$E_{b1} = V - I_{a1}R_a = 240 - 20 \times 0.5 = 230 \text{ volt}$$

At 1000 rpm,
$$E_{b2} = 240 - 0.5 I_{a2}$$

Now
$$I_{a2} = (I_{f1}I_{a1})/I_{f2} = \frac{40}{I_{f2}}$$

and
$$E_{b2} = \frac{I_{f2}N_2 E_{b1}}{I_{f1}N_1} = \frac{I_{f2} \times 1000 \times 230}{2 \times 500} = 230 I_{f2}$$

$\therefore \qquad\qquad 230 I_{f2} = 240 - 0.5 \dfrac{40}{I_{f2}}$

$$230 I_{f2}^2 - 240 I_{f2} + 20 = 0$$

Solving for I_{f2},

$$I_{f2} = 0.52 \pm (0.2724 - 0.0867)^{1/2} \quad \text{or} \quad \frac{12 \pm (144 - 46)^{1/2}}{23}$$

$$= 0.52 \pm 0.43$$

$$= 0.95 \quad \text{(neglecting the trivial solution)}$$

Hence,

$$\text{new } R_f = \frac{240}{0.95} = 252 \text{ ohm}$$

$\therefore$ Added $R_f = 252 - 120 = 132 \text{ ohm}$

Part (b).   At constant torque, max O/P occurs at max speed. Now,

$$\text{power output} = \omega\widehat{T} = VI_a - I_a^2 R_a$$

$$\frac{d\omega}{dI_a} = \frac{1}{\widehat{T}}(V - 2I_a R_a) = 0 \quad \text{for maximum}$$

The condition is thus, $V = 2I_a R_a$ or $I_a = V/2R_a$.

Substituting numerical values, at max O/P,

$$I_a = V/2R_a = \frac{240}{2 \times 0.5} = 240 \text{ amp}$$

$\therefore$ $E_b = V - I_a R_a = 240 - 240 \times 0.5 = 120 \text{ volt}$

From Part (a) we can write,

$$\frac{E_{b1}}{E_{b2}} = \frac{I_{a2} N_1}{I_{a1} N_2}$$

Hence

$$N = \frac{E_b I_a N_1}{E_{b1} I_{a1}} = \frac{120 \times 240 \times 500}{230 \times 20}$$

$$= 3130 \text{ rpm at max output}$$

N.B.   Practical limitations, e.g. commutation, circuit breakers, etc., would hardly permit the theoretical maximum to be reached for this machine.

Example 22

A d.c. shunt motor has speed control provided by a field rheostat. Show that the armature current is independent of speed for the condition of constant output power, (gross).

Solution

Using conventional notation, for constant power we have,

$$\omega_1 \textcircled{T}_1 = \omega_2 \textcircled{T}_2 \quad \therefore \quad \textcircled{T}_1/\textcircled{T}_2 = \omega_2/\omega_1$$

But

$$\frac{\textcircled{T}_1}{\textcircled{T}_2} = \frac{\Phi_1 I_1}{\Phi_2 I_2}$$

$\therefore$

$$\frac{I_1}{I_2} = \frac{\textcircled{T}_1 \Phi_2}{\textcircled{T}_2 \Phi_1} = \frac{\omega_2 \Phi_2}{\omega_1 \Phi_1}$$

Then

$$\frac{E_1}{E_2} = \frac{\omega_1 \Phi_1}{\omega_2 \Phi_2} = \frac{I_2}{I_1}$$

For a d.c. motor, $V = E + IR$. Hence

$$\frac{E_1}{E_2} = \frac{V - I_1 R}{V - I_2 R} = \frac{I_2}{I_1}$$

Cross multiplying, we can write,

$$I_2^2 R - I_2 V + I_1(V - I_1 R) = 0$$

Rearranging we have, $\quad (I_2^2 - I_1^2)R + (I_1 - I_2)V = 0$

Since V and R are constants the above can only be true if the factor $(I_1 - I_2) = 0$ or $I_1 = I_2$. This is independent of speed.

Example 23

A d.c. shunt motor runs normally on no load at 1520 rpm. (i) The armature and field circuits are suddenly open-circuited and the speed drops, reaching 1480 rpm after 40 seconds. (ii) When the armature only is open-circuited the speed reaches 1480 rpm after 25 seconds. (iii) When the armature only is suddenly switched from the supply to a load, the same decrease in speed occurs in 20 seconds and the average power dissipated in the load is 1 kW Calculate:
    (a) the moment of inertia of the armature,
    (b) the core losses corresponding to a speed of 1500 rpm.

Solution

Part (*a*).   Change in stored energy in the armature,

$$W = \tfrac{1}{2}J(\omega_1^2 - \omega_2^2)$$

$$= \frac{1}{2}J\left(\frac{2\pi}{60}\right)^2 (N_1^2 - N_2^2)$$

where N = rpm and J = moment of inertia.

Then,

$$W = \frac{1}{2}J\left(\frac{4\pi^2}{3600}\right)(1520 + 1480)(1520 - 1480)$$

$$= J \times \frac{\pi^2 \times 1.2 \times 10^5}{1800} = 658J \text{ N m or joule}$$

$$\text{Power (i)} = \text{friction losses} = \frac{658J}{40} \text{ watt}$$

$$\text{Power (ii)} = \text{friction + core losses} = \frac{658J}{25} \text{ watt}$$

$$\text{Power (iii)} = \text{friction + core losses} + 1000 = \frac{658J}{20} \text{ watt}$$

Hence,

$$P(\text{iii}) - P(\text{ii}) = 1000 = 658J(\tfrac{1}{20} - \tfrac{1}{25})$$

$$= 6.58J$$

$$\therefore \qquad J = \frac{1000}{6.58} = 152 \text{ kg m}^2$$

Part (b).   At 1500 rpm, (mean speed),

$$P(\text{ii}) - P(\text{i}) = 658 \times 152(\tfrac{1}{25} - \tfrac{1}{40})$$

$$= 658 \times 152 \times 0.015$$

$$= 1500 \text{ watt}$$

Example 24

A 2-pole, 210 V d.c. machine, operating as a shunt motor, on full load takes a line current of 101 amp, and runs at a speed of 900 rpm. The machine has armature resistance, $R_a = 0.1$ ohm, and field resistance, $R_f = 210$ ohm. On no load the line current is 11 amp. Calculate:

(a) the rotational inductance coefficient, G,

(b) the viscous damping coefficient,

(c) (i) the speed/time relationship if the starter resistance = 1.4 ohm, (ii) the time from start for the armature current to fall to 100 amp, and the speed at this instant. Take the inertia of the armature and the load = 1.2 kg m².

Solution (Ref. 2, p. 126, Ref. 3, p. 435)

Part (a).   Full-load armature current

$$I_a = I_L - I_f = 101 - \frac{210}{210} = 100 \text{ amp}$$

Volts generated in armature,

$$E_g = V - I_a R_a = 210 - 100(0.1) = 200 \text{ volts} = \omega M_d i_f$$

$$\omega = 2\pi N/60 = 30\pi \text{ rad/sec}$$

For a d.c. machine,

$$G = M_d = \frac{200}{30\pi \times 1.0} = 2.123 \text{ H/rad}$$

Part (b).   On no load,
$$I_a = I_L - I_f = 10 \text{ amp}$$
Then
$$E_g = V - I_a R_a = 210 - 10(0.1) = 209 \text{ volt}$$

$$\therefore \qquad \omega_0 = \frac{209}{M_d I_f} = \frac{209}{(2.123)(1.0)} = 98.45 \text{ rad/sec}$$

Armature power developed on no load $= E_g I_a = 209 \times 10$

$$= 2090 \text{ watt} = \omega_0 \textcircled{T} = \text{rotational losses}$$

$$\therefore \qquad \textcircled{T} = \frac{2090}{98.45} = \omega_0 D = \text{viscous damping torque}$$

Hence

$$\text{Damping coefficient}, D = \frac{2090}{(98.45)^2} = 0.216 \text{ Nm sec/rad}$$

Part (c).   (i) On load, neglecting L_a,

$$V = \omega M_d i_f + i_a R_a = \omega K_f + i_a R_a$$

where $K_f = M_d i_f = $ constant.

$$\therefore \qquad\qquad i_a = \frac{V - \omega K_f}{R_a}$$

Torque of electrical origin,

$$\textcircled{T}_e = M_d i_f i_a = K_f i_a = \frac{K_f V - \omega K_f^2}{R_a}$$

Also $\textcircled{T}_e = Jp\omega + D\omega$ where $p = \mathrm{d}/\mathrm{d}t$.

Collecting terms in ω,

$$\omega = \frac{K_f V}{R_a} \left[\frac{1}{Jp + D_e} \right] = \frac{K_f V}{R_a D_e} \left[\frac{1}{1 + T_m p} \right]$$

where

$$D_e = \left(D + \frac{K_f^2}{R_a}\right) \quad \text{and} \quad T_m = J/D_e$$

Substituting numerical values,

$$K_f = M_d i_f = 2.123 \times 1.0 = 2.123$$

$$K_f^2/R_a = 4.506/1.5 = 3.00$$

∴

$$D_e = (D + K_f^2/R_a) = 0.217 + 3.01 = 3.227$$

$$T_m = J/D_e = 1.2/3.216$$

Hence

$$\omega = \frac{2.123 \times 210}{1.5 \times 3.216}\left[\frac{1}{1 + (1.2/3.216)p}\right]$$

$$= 92.4(1 - \epsilon^{-2.68t})$$

(ii)

$$i_a = \frac{V - \omega K_f}{R_a} = \frac{V}{R_a} - \frac{K_f}{R_a}\left[\frac{K_f V}{D_e R_a (1 + T_m p)}\right]$$

$$= \frac{V}{R_a}\left[1 - \frac{K_f^2}{R_a D_e}\frac{1}{(1 + T_m p)}\right]$$

This can be simplified to,

$$i_a = \frac{V}{R_a}\epsilon^{-t/T_m}$$

if frictional damping D is neglected.

With numerical values, hence,

$$i_a = \frac{210}{1.5}\epsilon^{-2.68t} = 140\epsilon^{-2.68t}$$

$$= 100, \text{(given) at the required time.}$$

Thus

$$2.68t = l_n \frac{140}{100}$$

$$t = \frac{1}{2.68}l_n 1.4 = \frac{2.3026 \times 0.146\,13}{2.68}$$

$$= 0.125 \text{ sec}$$

Also

$$\omega_t = 92.4(1 - \epsilon^{-2.68t}) = 92.4(1 - \epsilon^{-0.3377})$$

$$= 92.4(1 - 0.7134) = 26.5 \text{ rad/sec}$$

$$= \frac{2\pi N}{60}$$

Hence
$$N_t = 253 \text{ rpm}$$

Example 25

A d.c. series motor has a load torque (T) given by $\text{(T)} = KN^{2.5}$, where $N =$ motor speed. Calculate the percentage change in supply voltage necessary to reduce the motor speed by one third. Assume magnetic linearity for the field and neglect the motor ohmic resistance.

Solution

Given $\text{(T)} = KN^{2.5}$

$$\text{The required ratio} = \frac{\text{initial speed}}{\text{final speed}} = \frac{N_1}{N_2} = \frac{3}{2}$$

$$\text{Then the ratio} \frac{\text{initial torque}}{\text{final torque}} = \frac{\text{(T)}_1}{\text{(T)}_2} = \frac{3^{2.5}}{2^{2.5}} = \frac{15.588}{5.657}$$

$$= 2.756$$

Now for a series motor $\text{(T)} \propto \Phi I$ and since $\Phi \propto I$, (given)

$$\therefore \qquad\qquad \text{(T)} \propto I^2$$

Hence
$$\frac{\text{(T)}_1}{\text{(T)}_2} = \frac{I_1^2}{I_2^2} = 2.756$$

Also, 'back' emf $E \propto \Phi N$. Then

$$\frac{E_1}{E_2} = \frac{\Phi_1 N_1}{\Phi_2 N_2} = \frac{I_1 N_1}{I_2 N_2}$$

Substituting from above,

$$\frac{E_1}{E_2} = \frac{3}{2} \times (2.756)^{1/2} = 2.49$$

Neglecting motor ohmic resistance, $V = E$. Then

$$\frac{V_1}{V_2} = \frac{E_1}{E_2} = 2.49$$

Thus

$$\text{New supply voltage, } V_2 = \frac{1}{2.49} V_1 = 0.4 V_1$$

$$= 40\% \text{ of original supply voltage}$$

Example 26

A 400 V d.c. series motor runs at 500 rpm when taking a line current of 50 amp. The armature resistance, $R_a = 0.2$ ohm and the field resistance, $R_f = 0.1$ ohm. Determine the value of field diverter-resistance required to increase the speed to 750 rpm. Assume constant torque and linear magnetization.

Solution

Initially,
$$E_1 = V - I_a(R_a + R_f) = 400 - 50(0.2 + 0.1)$$
$$= 385 \text{ volt}$$

$$\text{Torque} = kI_f I_a = 2500k = \text{constant}$$

At the new speed, let

$$I = \text{new line current}, \quad R = \text{diverter resistance}$$

Then,

$$\text{new } I_f = I\left(\frac{R}{0.1 + R}\right)$$

∴

$$\text{new torque} = kI^2\left(\frac{R}{0.1 + R}\right) = \text{constant}$$

$$kI^2\left(\frac{R}{0.1 + R}\right) = 2500k$$

Hence we may write,

$$I^2 = \frac{2500}{K} \quad \text{and} \quad I = \frac{50}{K^{1/2}}$$

where

$$K = \left(\frac{R}{0.1 + R}\right)$$

Also,

$$\text{new } I_f = 50K^{1/2}$$

Now,

$$\text{new machine resistance} = 0.2 + \left(\frac{0.1R}{0.1 + R}\right) = 0.2 + 0.1K$$

$$E_2 = 400 - \frac{50}{K^{1/2}}(0.2 + 0.1K)$$

$$= 400 - \frac{10}{K^{1/2}} - 5K^{1/2}$$

$$E \propto NI_f$$

$$\therefore \qquad E_2 = E_1 \left(\frac{N_2 I_{f2}}{N_1 I_{f1}}\right) = \frac{385 \times 750 \times 50 K^{1/2}}{500 \times 50}$$

$$= 577.5 K^{1/2}$$

Thus,

$$577.5 K^{1/2} = 400 - \frac{10}{K^{1/2}} - 5 K^{1/2}$$

$$577.5 K = 400 K^{1/2} - 10 - 5K$$

$$582.5 K - 400 K^{1/2} + 10 = 0$$

Then

$$K^{1/2} = \frac{400 \pm (160\,000 - 23\,300)^{1/2}}{1165} = \frac{400 \pm 370}{1165}$$

$$= 0.66 \quad \text{(neglecting trivial solution)}$$

$$K = 0.436$$

$$= \left(\frac{R}{0.1 + R}\right)$$

$$R = 0.0436 + 0.436R$$

Hence

$$R = 0.0773 \text{ ohm}$$

N.B.

$$\text{New line current} = I = \frac{50}{K^{1/2}} = \frac{50}{0.66} = 75.8 \text{ amp}$$

Example 27

A 50 kW, 240 V, 4-pole d.c. generator has a lap-connected armature winding having 420 conductors. Interpoles are to be added to give an airgap flux density of 0.3 Wb/m² at full load. The airgap at the interpoles is to be 1.4 cm long and this gap coefficient may be assumed 1.15. Estimate the number of turns on each interpole. Reluctance of the iron is neglected.

Solution

Full-load armature current, $I_a = (50 \times 10^3)/240 = 208$ amp. Ampere-turns on the airgap = $H_g l_g K$ where K = gap coeff. This will be the difference of the armature AT/pole and the interpole AT. Hence,

$$\text{Interpole } AT = \text{Armature } AT + \frac{B_g}{\mu_0} l_g K$$

$$= \frac{Z I_a}{4 a p} + \frac{B_g}{\mu_0} l_g K$$

$$= \frac{420 \times 208}{4 \times 4 \times 2} + \frac{0.3 \times 10^7}{4\pi} \times 0.014 \times 1.15$$

$$= 2730 + 3842 = 6572$$

$$\therefore \qquad \text{Required interpole turns} = \frac{6572}{208} = 31.6$$

$$= 32 \text{ turns}$$

Example 28

A separately-excited 2-pole d.c. generator has constants $R_a = 0.1$ ohm $L_a = 0.005$ H, $R_f = 100$ ohm $L_f = 20$ H, and $M_d = 0.8$ H.

(a) Calculate the transfer function of the machine operating on open circuit when it is driven at the normal speed of 35 πrad/sec.

(b) If a load having $R = 1.4$ ohm and $L = 0.01$ H is connected to the armature, calculate the time-variation of armature current when 150 V d.c. is suddenly applied to the field. Assume a linear magnetisation curve.

Solution

Part (a)   (Ref. 2, p. 128, Ref. 3, p. 437)

$$\text{The transfer function on O.C.} = \frac{\text{armature volts}}{\text{field volts}}.$$

The time-dependent equation for the field can be expressed,

$$V_f = i_f R_f + L_f \, di_f/dt = i_f(R_f + L_f p) \quad \text{where} \quad p = d/dt$$

$$\therefore \qquad i_f = \frac{V_f}{R_f}\left(\frac{1}{1 + T_f p}\right) \quad \text{where} \quad T_f = L_f/R_f$$

Armature generated volts,

$$e = \omega M_d i_f = K_g i_f$$

where K_g = slope of magnetization curve at speed ω.

$$\therefore \qquad e = K_g i_f = \frac{K_g V_f}{R_f}\left(\frac{1}{1 + T_f p}\right)$$

Hence,

$$\text{O.C. Transfer Function} = \frac{e}{V_f} = \frac{K_g}{R_f}\left(\frac{1}{1 + T_f p}\right)$$

Substituting numerical values,

$$T_f = L_f/R_f = 0.2 \text{ sec}$$

Then

$$\frac{e}{V_f} = \frac{35\pi \times 0.8}{100}\left(\frac{1}{1+0.2p}\right) = 0.88\left(\frac{1}{1+0.2p}\right)$$

Part (b). Now

$$i_a = \frac{e}{R_a + R}\left(\frac{1}{1+T_a p}\right) \quad \text{where} \quad T_a = \frac{L_a + L}{R_a + R}$$

Substituting numerical values,

$$i_a = \frac{0.88}{1.5}\left[\frac{1}{(1+0.2p)}\right]\left[\frac{1}{(1+0.01p)}\right]V_f$$

With $V_f = 150$ volts suddenly applied,

$$i_a = \frac{0.88 \times 150}{1.5}\left[\frac{1}{(1+0.2p)(1+0.01p)}\right]$$

$$= 88\left[\frac{1}{(1+0.2p)(1+0.01p)}\right]$$

This is a second order system with a solution of the form,

$$i_a = 88 + A e^{-t/T_f} + B e^{-t/T_a}$$

Now *either*

$$\text{at } t=0, i_a = 0 \quad \text{and} \quad 0 = 88 + A + B$$

$$di_a/dt = 0 \quad \text{and} \quad 0 = -5A - 100B$$

Solving for A and B,

$$A = -92.6 \qquad B = 4.63$$

$$\therefore \qquad i_a = 88 - 92.6\,e^{-5t} + 4.63\,e^{-100t}$$

or using partial fractions,

$$i_a = I_{ss}\left[1 - \frac{T_f}{T_f - T_a}e^{-t/T_f} - \frac{T_a}{T_a - T_f}e^{-t/T_a}\right]$$

$$= 88\left[1 - \frac{0.2}{0.2 - 0.01}e^{-5t} - \frac{0.01}{0.01 - 0.2}e^{-100t}\right]$$

$$= 88(1 - 1.052\,e^{-5t} + 0.0526\,e^{-100t})$$

$$= 88 - 92.6\,e^{-5t} + 4.63\,e^{-100t}$$

Example 29

Determine expressions for the transient behaviour of speed and armature current of a separately-excited d.c. motor following direct application of armature supply voltage. State any approximations.

Solution (Ref. 2, p. 130, Ref. 3, p. 443)

Assuming linearity, the time-dependent equations may be stated,

$$\left|\begin{matrix} V_f \\ V_a \end{matrix}\right| = \left|\begin{matrix} R_f + L_f p & M_d \\ \omega M_d & R_a + L_a p \end{matrix}\right| \times \left|\begin{matrix} i_f \\ i_a \end{matrix}\right|$$

For constant field current, we have,

$$V_a = \omega M_d i_f + (R_a + L_a p) i_a$$

$$= \omega K_f + (R_a + L_a p) i_a$$

where $p = d/dt$ and $K_f = M_d i_f = $ constant.

The torque of electrical origin,

$$Ⓣ_e = M_d i_f i_a = K_f i_a$$

$$= Jp\omega + D\omega + Ⓣ_s$$

where $J = $ moment of inertia of armature and $D = $ viscous friction.

Assuming L_a is negligible, and shaft torque $Ⓣ_s = 0$,

$$i_a = \frac{V_a - \omega K_f}{R_a}$$

$$Ⓣ_e = K_f i_a = \left|\frac{K_f V_a - \omega K_f^2}{R_a}\right| = (Jp + D)\omega$$

Collecting terms,

$$\left(Jp + D + \frac{K_f^2}{R_a}\right)\omega = \frac{K_f V_a}{R_a}$$

Hence

$$\omega = \frac{K_f V_a}{R_a}\left(\frac{1}{Jp + D_e}\right) = \frac{K_f V_a}{R_a D_e}\left(\frac{1}{1 + T_m p}\right)$$

where

$$D_e = \text{effective damping} = D + K_f^2/R_a$$

and

$$T_m = \text{mechanical time constant} = J/D_e$$

Then

$$\omega = \frac{K_f V_a}{R_a D_e}(1 - \epsilon^{-t/T_m}) = \omega_{ss}(1 - \epsilon^{-t/T_m})$$

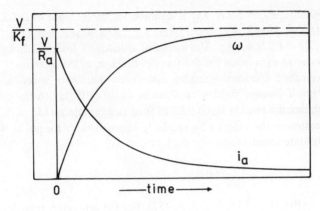

Fig. 29

Commonly D, the frictional damping, can be neglected, giving

$$D_e = K_f^2/R_a, \quad T_m = JR_a/K_f^2 \quad \text{and} \quad \omega_{ss} = V_a/K_f$$

For the armature current we have,

$$i_a = \frac{V_a - \omega K_f}{R_a}$$

Now

$$\omega = \omega_{ss}(1 - \epsilon^{-t/T_m}) = \frac{V_a}{K_f}(1 - \epsilon^{-t/T_m})$$

$$\frac{\omega K_f}{R_a} = \frac{V_a K_f}{K_f R_a}(1 - \epsilon^{-t/T_m}) = \frac{V_a}{R_a}(1 - \epsilon^{-t/T_m})$$

Hence,

$$i_a = \frac{V_a}{R_a} - \frac{V_a}{R_a}(1 - \epsilon^{-t/T_m}) = \frac{V_a}{R_a}\epsilon^{-t/T_m}$$

This solution applies directly to a 2-pole machine.

Note that

$$\omega = \text{electrical radian/sec} = \text{mechanical radian/sec}$$

But for a machine with P pairs of poles, $\omega = P\omega_m$ where $\omega_m = $ mechanical rad/sec.

Example 30

A separately-excited constant-speed d.c. generator supplies armature current to a constant-field d.c. motor to form a simple Ward–Leonard system of speed control. The machine specifications are: *Generator. $R_{ag} = 0.3$ ohm,*

$R_{fg} = 150$ ohm, $L_{fg} = 7.5$ H. L_{ag} is assumed negligible. Slope of O.C.C., $K_g = 1200$ volt/amp. *Motor* $R_{am} = 0.7$ ohm, L_{am} is assumed negligible. Torque constant, $K_f = 1.5$ N m/amp. The inertia of armature + load = 2.25 kg m².

(a) Derive an expression for the transfer function of the system.

(b) Neglecting frictional damping, determine the motor speed as a function of time following sudden application of 30 volts d.c. to the generator field. Estimate the time to reach 98% of final steady-state speed.

(c) Determine the effect of a suddenly imposed shaft torque of 9 Nm on the steady-state speed.

Solution

Part (a).   (Ref. 2, p. 135, Ref. 3, p. 452). For the generator, time-dependent equations are,

$$i_f = \frac{V_f}{R_{fg}} \left(\frac{1}{1 + T_{fg}p} \right) \quad \text{where} \quad T_{fg} = L_{fg}/R_{fg}$$

$$\therefore \qquad e_g = K_g i_f$$

where $K_g = \omega_g M_d$ for the generator = const.

$$e_g = \frac{K_g V_f}{R_{fg}} \left(\frac{1}{1 + T_{fg}p} \right)$$

For the motor, total armature circuit resistance, $R_A = R_{ag} + R_{am}$

$$i_a = \frac{e_g - \omega K_f}{R_A}$$

where $K_f = M_d i_f$ for the motor = constant.

Torque of electrical origin,

$$\textcircled{T}_e = K_f i_a$$

$$= \frac{K_f e_g - \omega K_f^2}{R_A} = Jp\omega + D\omega + \textcircled{T}_s$$

$$\therefore \qquad \omega \left(Jp + D + \frac{K_f^2}{R_A} \right) = \frac{K_f e_g}{R_A} - \textcircled{T}_s$$

Now, let $D_e = D + K_f^2/R_A$ = effective damping

$$\therefore \qquad \omega = \frac{1}{D_e} \left(\frac{K_f e_e}{R_A} - \textcircled{T}_s \right) \left(\frac{1}{1 + T_m p} \right) \qquad (1)$$

where $T_m = J/D_e$ = mechanical time constant.

Taking $\text{(T)}_s = 0$ and let J = inertia of arm + load

$$\omega = \frac{K_f e_g}{D_e R_A} \frac{1}{(1 + T_m p)}$$

Substituting for e_g from above,

$$\frac{\omega}{V_f} = \frac{K_f K_g}{D_e R_A R_f} \left[\frac{1}{(1 + T_{fg}p)(1 + T_m p)} \right]$$

Part (b).   Substituting numerical values and with $D = 0$,

$$T_m = \frac{JR_A}{K_f^2} = \frac{2.25 \times 1.00}{(1.5)^2} = 1.0 \text{ sec}$$

$$T_{fg} = L_{fg}/R_{fg} = \frac{7.5}{150} = 0.05 \text{ sec}$$

With $D = 0, D_e = K_f^2/R_A$, then

$$\omega_{ss} = \frac{K_g K_f V_f}{D_e R_A R_f} = \frac{K_g V_f}{K_f R_f} = \frac{1200 \times 30}{1.5 \times 150} = 160 \text{ rad/sec}$$

The time-dependent solution is for a second-order system, hence,

$$\omega = \omega_{ss} + A e^{-t/T_{fg}} + B e^{-t/T_m}$$
$$= 160 + A e^{-20t} + B e^{-t}$$

Solving for A and B, at $t = 0$,

$$\omega = 0 \quad \text{and} \quad 0 = 160 + A + B$$

$$\frac{d\omega}{dt} = 0 \qquad \underline{ 0 = -20A - B}$$

$$A = 8.42$$

$$B = -168.4$$

$$\therefore \qquad \omega = 160 + 8.4 e^{-20t} - 168.4 e^{-t}$$

Note that the field time constant is relatively small and an approximate solution, with little significant error is,

$$\omega = 160(1 - e^{-t})$$

At 98% final speed, $e^{-t} = 0.02$

$$\therefore \qquad t = 3.9 \text{ sec}$$

Part (c).   Referring to Part (a), the effect of imposed (T)_s, when the set has reached steady-state, (see equation (1)),

$$\Delta\omega = \frac{\textcircled{T}_s}{D_e}\frac{1}{(1+T_mp)} \hat{=} \frac{\textcircled{T}_s R_A}{K_f^2}(1-\epsilon^{-t/T_m})$$

Substituting given values,

$$\text{Steady-state } \Delta\omega = -\frac{9 \times 1.0}{(1.5)^2} = -4$$

∴ $$\omega = 160 - 4(1-\epsilon^{-t}) = 156 + 4\epsilon^{-t} \text{ rad/sec}$$

i.e., the speed falls exponentially to 156 rad/sec.

Example 31

Using generalized-machine theory determine an expression for the transient behaviour of armature current due to sudden short-circuit of the armature of a separately-excited d.c. generator, running normally on open-circuit. Allow for the effects of armature reaction. Hence calculate and sketch the transient s.c. current for a 4-pole, 200 V, 300 rpm separately-excited d.c. generator having the following constants; $R_f = 286$, $L_f = 8$ H, $M_f = 4.55$ H, $R_a = 0.1$, $L_a = 0.0019$ H. Armature reaction is estimated equivalent to a differential-compound series-field winding having $M_s = 0.05$ H.

Solution   (Ref. 5, p. 67, Ref. 2, p. 127)

In practice the large armature current on s.c. will cause magnetic saturation and non-linearity. A solution based on constant inductance coefficients will be approximate. Hence certain approximations may be admissible which will simplify the mathematics, but maintain the essential character and the approximate magnitude of the transient current.

For a simple d.c. generator, the time-dependent equations may be stated,

$$V_f = (R_f + L_f p)i_f$$
$$V_a = \omega M_f i_f + (R_a + L_a p)i_a$$

During s.c., speed is assumed to remain constant. Also V_f is constant. But in practice, the effect of armature reaction is considerable. Hence a more realistic solution is given by the case of a differential-compound series excitation in addition to the separately-excited shunt field. Allowing for this we have,

$$V_f = (R_f + L_f p)i_f + M_s p i_a$$
$$V_a = \omega M_f i_f + (R_a + L_a p)i_a + \omega M_s i_a + M_s p i_f$$

Assuming linear equations, with constant coefficients, the principle of superposition can be applied. The equations for superimposed transient variables, i_f' and i_a' can be written,

$$0 = (R_f + L_f p) i_f' + M_s p i_a'$$

$$-V_a = \omega M_f i_f' + [(\omega M_s + R_a) + L_a p] i_a' + M_s p i_f'$$

Zero replaces V_f and voltage cancellation simulates s.c., since V_f does not change and the s.c. is equivalent to a superimposed $-V_a$. Now the effect of $M_s p i_f'$ will be relatively small and the term may be neglected. The equations can be written,

$$0 = R_f(1 + T_f p) i_f' + M_s p i_a'$$

$$-V_a = K i_f' + R(1 + T_a p) i_a'$$

where $R = (R_a + \omega M_s)$, $T_a = L_a/R$ = effective arm time-constant. $K = \omega M_f$ and $T_f = L_f/R_f$ = field time-constant.

Now we have,

$$i_f' = \frac{-M_s p i_a'}{R_f(1 + T_f p)}$$

Then,

$$-V_a = \frac{-K M_s p i_a'}{R_f(1 + T_f p)} + R(1 + T_a p) i_a'$$

and

$$i_{sc} = -i_a' = \frac{V_a R_f(1 + T_f p)}{R R_f(1 + T_f p)(1 + T_a p) - K M_s p}$$

$$= \frac{V_a}{R} \left[\frac{(1 + T_f p)}{(1 + T_f p)(1 + T_a p) - \dfrac{K M_s p}{R R_f}} \right] \qquad (1)$$

This expression has a form which is characteristic of this type of problem. Recalling the Heavyside notation for unit step function, viz; $[Tp/(1 + Tp)] 1 = \epsilon^{-t/T}$, we assume factors for the denominator above, and an expansion by partial fractions for the expression in the brackets, thus,

$$\frac{1 + T_f p}{(1 + T_a' p)(1 + T_f' p)} = 1 - \frac{B T_a' p}{(1 + T_a' p)} - \frac{C T_f' p}{(1 + T_f' p)} \qquad (2)$$

$$= 1 - B \epsilon^{-t/T_a'} - C \epsilon^{-t/T_f'}$$

where the effective T_a' and T_f', and the constants B and C must now be evaluated.

(i) Let $T_a' = T_a/(1 - A)$, $T_f' = T_f(1 - A)$ where A is a constant. Now, equating the denominators of equations (1) and (2), we have, for the coefficient of the 'p' term,

$$T_a + T_f - \frac{KM_s}{RR_f} = (T'_a - T'_f)$$

$$= \frac{T_a}{(1-A)} + T_f(1-A) = \frac{T_a}{(1-A)} + T_f - AT_f$$

$$T_a - \frac{KM_s}{RR_f} = \frac{T_a}{(1-A)} - AT_f$$

$$T_a - AT_a - \frac{KM_s}{RR_f}(1-A) = T_a - A(1-A)T_f$$

Since $T_a \ll T_f$ we can approximate by neglecting the T_a term. Then,

$$A = \frac{1}{T_f}(KM_s/RR_f) = KM_s/L_f R$$

Hence

$$T'_a = T_a \left/ \left(1 - \frac{KM_s}{L_f R}\right) \right. \quad \text{and} \quad T'_f = T_f\left(1 - \frac{KM_s}{L_f R}\right)$$

(ii) Multiply both sides of equation (2) by $(1 + T'_a p)$ to give,

$$\frac{(1 + T_f p)}{(1 + T'_f p)} = (1 + T'_a p) - BT'_a p - \frac{CT'_f p(1 + T'_a p)}{(1 + T'_f p)}$$

Now put $p = -1/T'_a$. Then

$$B = \left(1 - \frac{T_f}{T'_a}\right) \left/ \left(1 - \frac{T'_f}{T'_a}\right) \right. = \left(\frac{T'_a - T_f}{T'_a - T'_f}\right)$$

Similarly, by multiplying (2) by $(1 + T'_f)$ and then putting $p = -1/T'_f$ we get

$$C = \left(\frac{T'_f - T_f}{T'_f - T'_a}\right)$$

Referring to the exponential form of equation (2), the values for B and C can be further simplified by neglecting T'_a compared with T_f or T'_f, giving a final form for equation (1),

$$i_{sc} = \frac{V_a}{R} + \left(\frac{V_a}{R'} - \frac{V_a}{R}\right) \epsilon^{-t/T'_f} - \frac{V_a}{R'}\epsilon^{-t/T'_a}$$

where

$$R' = \frac{T'_f}{T_f} R = \left(R - \frac{KM_s}{L_f}\right)$$

and called Transient Resistance.

$$T'_a = L_a/R' \quad \text{and} \quad T'_f = T_f(R'/R)$$

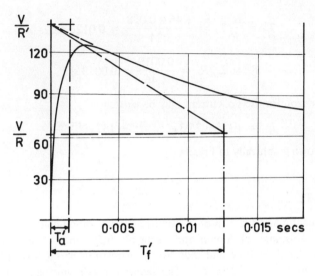

Fig. 31

Numerical part.   Using given values, speed = 300 rpm, pairs of poles $P = 2$

∴ $\omega_m = 10\pi$ mech rad/sec

and

$$\omega = P\omega_m = 20\pi \text{ elect rad/sec}$$

On steady O.C., $V_a = \omega M_f i_f = 200$ volt, (given)

∴ $i_f = 200/(20\pi \times 4.55) = 0.7$ amp

Hence

$$R_f = V_a/i_f = 200/0.7 = 286 \text{ ohm}$$

$$T_f = L_f/R_f = 8/286 = 0.028 \text{ sec}$$

$$K = \omega M_f = 20\pi \times 4.55 = 286$$

$$R = (R_a + \omega M_s) = 0.1 + (20\pi \times 0.05) = 3.24$$

$$R' = \left[R - \frac{KM_s}{L_f}\right] = 3.24 - \frac{286 \times 0.05}{8} = 3.24 - 1.78 = 1.46$$

Hence

$$\frac{V_a}{R} = \frac{200}{3.24} = 61.7 \text{ amp}$$

$$\frac{V_a}{R'} = \frac{200}{1.46} = 137.0 \text{ amp}$$

$$T'_f = \frac{R'}{R} T_f = \frac{1.46 \times 0.028}{3.24} = 0.0126 \text{ sec}$$

$$T'_a = L_a/R' = \frac{0.0019}{1.46} = 0.0013 \text{ sec}$$

The expression for the s.c. current may be written,

$$i_{sc} = 61.7 + 75.3\, \epsilon^{-t/0.0126} - 137\, \epsilon^{-t/0.0013}$$

This is shown graphically in Fig. 31

Example 32

A permanent-magnet d.c. motor employed in a position-control system has armature resistance of 5 ohm and negligible inductance. The motor constants are 0.25 V/rad/sec and 0.25 Nm/A. Armature inertia is 0.01 Nm/sec² and load inertia is 9.0 Nm/sec². The required maximum load is 10 Nm at 10 rad/sec and the position error is to be less than 0.05 radian when the input changes at 10 rad/sec. If the permitted maximum armature applied voltage is 50 volt, determine:

(a) a suitable gear ratio between the motor and the load,

(b) a suitable amplifier.

(c) Examine the stability and modify the system with velocity feedback to meet a specification of a maximum overshoot of 20% to a step input.

Solution   (Ref. 2, p. 130)

Part (a).   For a d.c. motor,

where $p = \mathrm{d}/\mathrm{d}t$

$$V = \omega M_d i_f + i_a R_a + L_a p i_a$$
$$= \omega K_f + i_a R_a$$

for constant field and negligible L_a

$$\therefore \qquad i_a = \frac{(V - \omega K_f)}{R_a}$$

Armature power developed $= e_a i_a = \omega K_f i_a$

$$= \frac{\omega K_f}{R_a}(V - \omega K_f) = \frac{\omega K_f V - \omega^2 K_f^2}{R_a} = P$$

$$\frac{\mathrm{d}P}{\mathrm{d}\omega} = \frac{K_f}{R_a}(V - 2\omega K_f) = 0 \quad \text{for maximum } P$$

that is, $V = 2\omega K_f$

$\therefore$ Maximum power occurs when $\omega = \dfrac{V}{2K_f}$ and $P_{max} = \dfrac{V^2}{4R_a}$

With the given figures,

$$P_{max} = \frac{(50)^2}{4 \times 5} = 125 \text{ watt}$$

At P_{max},

$$\omega = \frac{V}{2K_f} = \frac{50}{2 \times 0.25} = 100 \text{ rad/sec}$$

Required max load $= 10\,\text{Nm at } 10 \text{ rad/sec} = 100 \text{ watt}$

Choose a gear ratio of 10/1. Then,

$$\text{Referred load inertia, } J_L' = \frac{J_L}{N^2} = \frac{9}{100} = 0.09$$

$\therefore$ $J_m + J_L' = 0.01 + 0.09 = 0.10$

Part (b).   Now motor torque,

$$\widehat{T} = K_f i_a = \frac{K_f V - \omega K_f^2}{R_a}$$

also

$$= (Jp + D)\,\omega$$

where $D =$ frictional damping.

Equating right-hand sides, and transposing,

$$\frac{K_f V}{R_a} = \left[Jp + \left(D + \frac{K_f^2}{R_a} \right) \right]\omega$$

$$= \left(Jp + \frac{K_f^2}{R_a} \right)\omega$$

when D is negligible.

Then machine transfer function,

$$\omega/V = \frac{K_f}{R_a}\left(\frac{1}{Jp + D_e} \right) \quad \text{where} \quad D_e = \frac{K_f^2}{R_a}$$

Substituting given values,

$$\frac{\omega}{V} = \frac{0.25}{5}\left(\frac{1}{0.1p + 0.0125} \right) = \left(\frac{0.05}{0.1p + 0.0125} \right)$$

$$= \left(\frac{0.5}{p + 0.125} \right)$$

Allowing for gearing and an amplifier of gain A, we can draw a diagram;

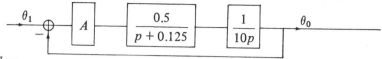

Now,

$$\text{Open-loop Transfer Function} = \frac{\theta_0}{\theta_1 - \theta_0} = G$$

Then

$$\frac{\text{error}}{\text{input}} = \frac{\theta_1 - \theta_0}{\theta_1} = \frac{1}{1 + G} = \frac{1}{1 + \dfrac{0.05A}{p(p + 0.125)}}$$

$$= \frac{p(p + 0.125)}{p(p + 0.125) + 0.05A}$$

Given that the input changes at $10\,\text{rad/sec} = p\theta_1$, then,

$$\Delta\,(\text{error}) = \Delta\varepsilon = \frac{10(p + 0.125)}{p(p + 0.125) + 0.05A}$$

$$\text{Limit } \varepsilon\,(\text{as } p \to 0) = \frac{1.25}{0.05A}$$

which is required $\leqslant 0.05$ (given)

$$\therefore \qquad\qquad\qquad A = 500$$

We can now draw the system diagram;

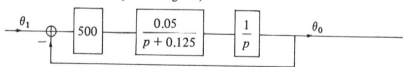

Now,

$$\text{Open-loop transfer function} = \frac{\theta_0}{\theta_1 - \theta_0} = G$$

$$= \frac{25}{p(p + 0.125)}$$

$$\text{Closed-loop transfer function} = \frac{\theta_0}{\theta_1} = \frac{G}{1 + G}$$

$$= \frac{25}{p(p + 0.125)}\left[\frac{1}{1 + \dfrac{25}{p(p + 0.125)}}\right]$$

$$= \frac{25}{p(p + 0.125) + 25} = \frac{25}{p^2 + 0.125p + 25}$$

Note that the denominator gives the roots of the characteristic equation. In general notation, (viz. Example 8) it can be interpreted as $p^2 + 2\zeta\omega_n + \omega_n^2$. Hence we have,

$$\omega_n = 25^{1/2} = 5 \text{ rad/sec} \quad \text{and} \quad \zeta = \frac{0.125}{2 \times 5} = 0.0125$$

Part (c). Referring to Example 8,

$$\text{Max Overshoot} = e^{-\pi\zeta/(1-\zeta^2)^{1/2}}$$

Substituting our values,

$$\pi\zeta/(1 - \zeta^2)^{1/2} = 0.039\ 27$$

$$\text{Max overshoot} = e^{-0.039\ 27} = 0.96 \text{ per unit}$$

This would not be satisfactory.

For the proposed permissible overshoot of 20%,

$$e^{-\pi\zeta/(1-\zeta^2)^{1/2}} = 0.2$$

$$\left[\frac{-\pi\zeta}{(1 - \zeta^2)^{1/2}}\right]^2 = (1.609)^2 = 2.588$$

$$\zeta^2 = \frac{2.588}{\pi^2 + 2.588} \quad \text{and} \quad \zeta = 0.4557 \quad (\text{say } 0.46)$$

The system may be re-drawn, to allow for velocity feedback derived from a tachogenerator with volts constant K_g.

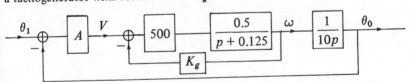

Now A and K_g are evaluated to give $\zeta = 0.46$.

Consider the inner loop, without K_g,

$$V = \left[\frac{(p + 0.125)}{250}\right]\omega$$

Adding ωK_g gives,

$$\frac{V}{\omega} = \frac{p + 0.125 + 250K_g}{250}$$

Then transfer function of inner loop with K_g,

$$\frac{\omega}{V} = \frac{250}{p + 0.125 + 250K_g}$$

Introducing amplifier gain, A and gearing $1/10p$, we have;

$$\text{Open-loop Transfer Function} = \frac{\theta_0}{\theta_1 - \theta_0} = G$$

$$= \frac{25A}{p(p + 0.125 + 250K_g)}$$

$$\text{Closed-loop transfer function} = \frac{G}{1 + G}$$

$$= \frac{25A}{p(p + 0.125 + 250K_g) + 25A}$$

Hence

$$\text{new } \omega_n^2 = 25A \quad \text{and} \quad \text{new } \zeta = \frac{250K_g + 0.125}{2(25A)^{1/2}}$$

Applying the given permissible error of 0.05 at $p\theta_1 = 10$ rad/sec

$$\frac{\theta_1 - \theta_0}{\theta_1} = \frac{\varepsilon}{\theta_1} = \frac{p(p + 0.125 + 250K_g)}{p(p + 0.125 + 250K_g) + 25A}$$

$$\text{Limit } \varepsilon \text{ (as } p \to 0) = \frac{10(250K_g + 0.125)}{25A} \leqslant 0.05 \quad \text{(given)}$$

$$\therefore \qquad A = \frac{200(250K_g + 0.125)}{25}$$

The other constraint is

$$\zeta^2 = (0.46)^2 = 0.212$$

$$= \left[\frac{250K_g + 0.125}{2(25A)^{1/2}} \right]^2$$

Substituting for A, (as determined above),

$$0.212 = \frac{(250K_g + 0.125)^2}{4 \times 200(250K_g + 0.125)} = \frac{250K_g + 0.125}{800}$$

$$250K_g = 169.6 - 0.125 = 169.475$$

$$\therefore \qquad K_g = \frac{169.475}{250} = 0.678 \text{ volt/rad/sec}$$

$$A = 8(250K_g + 0.125) = 1356 + 1 = 1357$$

Example 33

A Ward–Leonard speed control system is arranged as shown in the schematic diagram, Fig. 33. The system constants are given: *Generator* $L_f = 20\,\text{H}, R_f = 100\,\text{ohm}$, emf constant, $K_g = 500\,\text{V/A}$. *Motor* torque constant, $K_T = 2.5\,\text{Nm/A}$, emf constant, $K_e = 2.5\,\text{V/rad/s}$. Total armature circuit $R_a = 0.6\,\text{ohm}$, $L_a = 0.16\,\text{H}$ and inertia, $J = 2.5\,\text{kg m}^2$. Tachogenerator $K_t = 0.2\,\text{V/rad/s}$. It is required to determine:

(a) the transfer function between speed and control voltage assuming zero torque loading,

(b) the transfer function between change of speed and a load torque, assuming constant reference load,

(c) the amplifier gain to limit speed change to 2 rad/s when a steady load of 60 Nm is applied to the motor,

(d) the control voltage, with this amplifier gain, to give a no-load speed of 100 rad/s.

(e) Check the stability of the system.

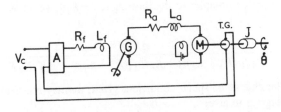

Fig. 33

Solution   (Ref. 2, p. 135)

Using standard notation the system may be represented, for analysis, by a block diagram indicating the inter-dependence of the several parts of the system, viz;

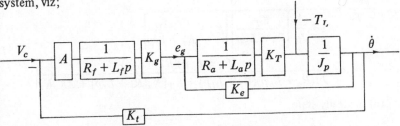

(a) Assuming zero load torque, the essential parts of the diagram can be simplified and reconsidered, viz;

Now, the effect of a feedback loop can be illustrated by considering the part of the system governed by the K_e loop. Without the loop, the forward-going sequence gives,

$$\dot{\theta} = \left[\frac{K_T}{R_a J p(1 + T_a p)} \right] e_g$$

where e_g = generator volts applied to armature and $T_a = L_a/R_a$.

Adding the K_e loop is equivalent to an additional input of $-\dot{\theta}K_e$, giving,

$$\dot{\theta} = \left[\frac{K_T}{R_a J p(1 + T_a p)} \right] (e_g - \dot{\theta}K_e)$$

Rearranging the equation to combine the speed, $\dot{\theta}$ terms,

$$\dot{\theta} \left[1 + \frac{K_e K_T}{R_a J p(1 + T_a p)} \right] = \left[\frac{K_T}{R_a J p(1 + T_a p)} \right] e_g$$

$$\therefore \qquad \dot{\theta} = \left[\frac{K_T}{R_a J p(1 + T_a p) + K_e K_T} \right] e_g$$

Applying the same principles to the loop signal, $-K_t\dot{\theta}$, we obtain the transfer function,

$$\frac{\dot{\theta}}{V_c} = \frac{A K_g K_T}{[J p(R_a + L_a p) + K_e K_T](R_f + L_f p) + A K_g K_T K_t}$$

(b) For the change of speed conditions given, we may re-orientate the system block diagram to give;

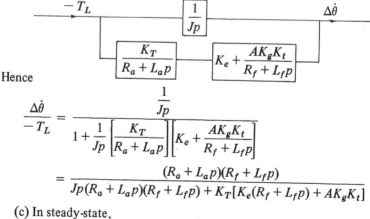

Hence

$$\frac{\Delta\dot{\theta}}{-T_L} = \frac{\dfrac{1}{Jp}}{1 + \dfrac{1}{Jp}\left[\dfrac{K_T}{R_a + L_a p}\right]\left[K_e + \dfrac{A K_g K_t}{R_f + L_f p}\right]}$$

$$= \frac{(R_a + L_a p)(R_f + L_f p)}{J p(R_a + L_a p)(R_f + L_f p) + K_T[K_e(R_f + L_f p) + A K_g K_t]}$$

(c) In steady-state,

$$\frac{\Delta\dot{\theta}}{-T_L} = \frac{R_a R_f}{K_T K_e R_f + A K_g K_t K_T}$$

$$= \frac{0.6 \times 100}{(2.5 \times 2.5 \times 100) + A(500 \times 0.2 \times 2.5)}$$

$$\frac{2}{60} = \frac{0.24}{(2.5 + A)}$$

$$A + 2.5 = 30 \times 0.24 = 7.2$$

$$\therefore \qquad \text{Amplifier Gain, } A = 7.2 - 2.5 = 4.7$$

(d) In steady-state, using the transfer function in Part (a),

$$\frac{\dot\theta}{V_c} = \frac{AK_gK_T}{K_TK_eR_f + AK_gK_TK_t} = \frac{AK_g}{K_eR_f + AK_gK_t}$$

$$= \frac{500 \times 4.7}{250 + 470} = 3.26$$

$$\therefore \qquad \text{Control Voltage, } V_c = \frac{\dot\theta}{3.26} = \frac{100}{3.26}$$

$$= 30.67 \text{ volt}$$

(e) Stability may be examined by consideration of the roots of the characteristic equation, given by the denominator of the transfer function in Part (a) above.

Substituting values, in this case,

$$[2.5p(0.6 + 0.16p) + 6.25](100 + 20p) + 4.7 \times 500 \times 2.5 \times 0.2 = 0$$

Collecting terms, gives,

$$8p^3 + 70p^2 + 275p + 1800 = 0$$

The Routh array, based on a general equation

$$a_0p^3 + a_1p^2 + a_2p + a_3 = 0$$

is given in the form,

$$
\begin{array}{c}
a_0 \qquad a_2 \\
a_1 \qquad a_3 \\
b_1
\end{array}
$$

and

$$b_1 = \frac{a_1a_2 - a_0a_3}{a_1}$$

Routh's criterion states that the number of sign changes in the first column of the array is equal to the number of roots with positive real parts.

The array in this example is:

$$
\begin{array}{cc}
8 & 275 \\
70 & 1800 \\
69.3 &
\end{array}
$$

There are no sign changes in the first column and hence the system is stable.

Example 34

A 6-pole series commutator motor develops a torque of 20 Nm when it is connected to 240 V, 50 Hz a.c. mains. The machine has the following constants; $R_a = 0.75\,\Omega$, $L_a = 0.01\,H$, $R_f = 1.0\,\Omega$, $L_f = 0.015\,H$, $M_{af} = 0.015\,H$. Latterly a series compensating winding is added to the machine. Assuming the load torque unchanged, it is required to determine the speed and power factor for the motor before and after the compensation. The new winding has $R_c = 0.5\,\Omega$, $L_c = 0.01\,H$ and a coupling coefficient of 0.9 with the armature winding.

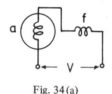

Fig. 34 (a)

Solution   (Ref. 2, p. 254)

(1) Before compensation, Fig. Ex. 34(a).
    The controlling equations can be expressed;

$$
\begin{vmatrix} v_f \\ v_a \end{vmatrix} = \begin{vmatrix} R_f + L_f p & 0 \\ \dot\theta M_{af} & R_a + L_a p \end{vmatrix} \times \begin{vmatrix} i_f \\ i_a \end{vmatrix}
$$

Also torque, $\textcircled{T}$ = (pole-pairs)$(M_{af} i_f i_a)$ = (pole-pairs)$(M_{af} i_a^2)$ since $i_f = i_a$.
Also $v = v_f + v_a$.
    For sinusoidal supply,

$$
V = [R_f + R_a + \dot\theta M_{af} + j\omega(L_a + L_f)] I_a
$$

With given data, torque = 20, hence

$$I_a = \left(\frac{20}{3 \times 0.015}\right)^{1/2} = 21.1 \text{ A}$$

Then

$$240 = 21.1[1.75 + 0.015\dot\theta + j(0.025 \times 314)]$$

$$\frac{V}{I_a} = [Z] = \frac{240}{21.1} = 11.37 = [R + jX] \qquad [modulus]$$

Then

$$R = 1.75 + 0.015\dot\theta \quad \text{and} \quad X = (0.025 \times 314) = 7.85$$

$$1.75 + 0.015\dot\theta = (Z^2 - X^2)^{1/2} = (11.37^2 - 7.85^2) = 8.2$$

$$\therefore \qquad \dot\theta = \frac{8.2 - 1.75}{0.015} = 430 \text{ elect rad/sec}$$

$$\dot\theta_{\text{mech}} = \dot\theta/(\text{pole-pairs}) = \frac{430}{3} = 143.3 \text{ rad/sec}$$

$$= \frac{143.3 \times 60}{2\pi} = 1368 \text{ rpm}$$

$$\text{Power Factor} = \cos\phi = \frac{R}{Z} = \frac{8.2}{11.37} = 0.722 \text{ lagging}$$

(2) After compensation, Fig. Ex. 34(b).

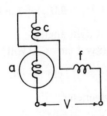

Fig. 34(b)

The controlling equations are now,

$$\begin{vmatrix} v_a \\ v_c \\ v_f \end{vmatrix} = \begin{vmatrix} R_a + L_a p & M_{ac} p & M_{af}\dot\theta \\ M_{ca} p & R_c + L_c p & 0 \\ 0 & 0 & R_f + L_f p \end{vmatrix} \times \begin{vmatrix} i_a \\ i_c \\ i_f \end{vmatrix}$$

and $i_a = i_f = -i_c$. Also $v = v_a + v_f - v_c$.

$$\therefore \qquad V = I_a[R_a + R_c + R_f + \dot\theta M_{af} + j\omega(L_a + L_f + L_c - 2M_{ca})]$$

For 0.9 coupling,

$$M_{ca} = 0.9(L_a \times L_c)^{1/2} = 0.9(0.01 \times 0.01)^{1/2} = 0.009$$

$(T) = 20\,\text{Nm}$, (as before) and so $I_a = 21.1\,\text{A}$.

$$\text{New } [Z] = \frac{240}{21.1} = [2.25 + 0.015\dot{\theta} + j314(0.035 - 0.018)]$$

Then
$$= [2.25 + 0.015\dot{\theta} + j5.34]$$
$$R = (Z^2 - X^2)^{1/2} = (129 - 28.5)^{1/2} = 10$$
$$2.25 + 0.015\dot{\theta} = 10$$

$$\text{New } \dot{\theta} = \frac{10 - 2.25}{0.015} = 516.7\,\text{elect rad/sec}$$

$$\text{New } \dot{\theta}_{\text{mech}} = 516.7/3 = 172.2\,\text{rad/sec}$$

$$= \frac{172.2 \times 60}{2\pi} = 1644\,\text{rpm}$$

$$\text{New power factor} = \frac{R}{Z} = \frac{10}{11.37} = 0.88\,\text{lagging}$$

Alternative solution   With sinusoidal a.c. supply, interpretation of the voltage components as phasors provides a rapid graphical method of solution. We have,

$$V = [(R_f + R_a + \dot{\theta}M_{af}) + j\omega(L_a + L_f)]I_a$$

The voltage components are at right angles.

Hence, with a volts scale, (say 1 cm = 20 volt) draw

$$v = 240\,\text{volts} = 12\,\text{cm} = OC \quad \text{(Fig. 34(c))}$$

Draw a semi-circle on OC as diameter.

$$\text{Transformer volts, } \omega(L_a + L_f)I_a = 314 \times 0.025 \times 21.1$$

Now
$$= 166\,\text{volt} = 8.3\,\text{cm} = CD$$

Then
$$I_a(R_f + R_a) = 21.1 \times 1.75 = 37\,\text{volts} = 1.85\,\text{cm} = DD'$$

$$OD' = \dot{\theta}M_{af}I_a = 6.8\,\text{cm} = 136\,\text{volt}$$

$$\therefore \quad \dot{\theta} = \frac{136}{21.1 \times 0.015} = 430\,\text{elect rad/sec}$$

$$= \frac{430}{3}\,\text{mech rad/sec} = 1370\,\text{rpm}$$

OD gives the direction of the current phasor, (in phase with the real component of V). By measurement,

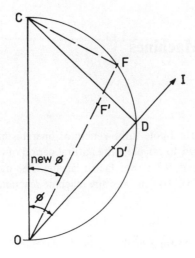

Fig. 34(c)

$$\phi = \underline{/\text{COD}} = 44° \quad \text{and} \quad \cos \phi = 0.72 \text{ lag}$$

After compensation

$$\omega(L_a + L_f + L_c - 2M_{ac})I_a = (314 \times 0.017)\,21.1$$

$$= 113 \text{ volt} = 5.65 \text{ cm} = CF$$

$$\text{New IR} = I_a(R_a + R_f + R_c) = 21.1 \times 2.25 = 47.4 \text{ volt.}$$

$$= 2.37 \text{ cm} = FF'$$

Then

$$OF' = 8.25 \text{ cm} = 165 \text{ volt} = \text{new } \dot{\theta}M_{af}I_a$$

$$\text{New } \dot{\theta} = \frac{165}{21.1 \times 0.015} = 521 \text{ elect rad/sec}$$

$$= \frac{521}{3} \text{ mech rad/sec} = 1658 \text{ rpm}$$

$$\underline{/\text{COF}} = \text{new } \phi = 28.3° \quad \text{and} \quad \text{new } \cos \phi = 0.88 \text{ lag}$$

Note that the Circle Diagram construction can give a wider appreciation of the performance of the machine over a range of conditions. The mechanical characteristics are similar to those of the d.c. series motor.

Chapter Four

Synchronous Machines

Example 35

A 60 MW 33 kV 50 Hz 4-pole turbo-generator operates in synchronism with the Grid. It is required to calculate the natural period of oscillation when the machine is on full load, 0.8 power factor lagging. The moment of inertia of the rotating mass is 35 000 kg m² and the machine reactance is 1.0 per unit.

Solution (Ref. 7, p. 258; Ref. 2, p. 196)

The dynamical equation for a small angular displacement, $\Delta\delta$ can be written,

$$Mp^2\Delta\delta + K_dp\Delta\delta + \left(\frac{\partial P}{\partial\delta}\right)\Delta\delta = \Delta P \quad \text{where} \quad p = \frac{d}{dt}$$

The characteristic equation is thus:

$$Mp^2 + K_dp + \left(\frac{\partial P}{\partial\delta}\right) = 0$$

Neglecting damping, K_d, the roots of the equation are,

$$p_1, p_2 = \pm j\sqrt{\left(\frac{\partial P}{\partial\delta}\right)\frac{1}{M}} = \pm j\omega_0$$

where ω_0 = natural angular frequency of oscillation.

$$\frac{\partial P}{\partial\delta} = P_{\text{syn}} = mVI_{sc}\theta \cos\delta \quad \text{watt/degree mech displacement}$$

with, (see Example 37), θ in electrical units,

$$\theta = 1° \text{ mech} = \text{(pole-pairs)}\left(\frac{\pi}{180}\right) \quad \text{electrical rad}$$

$$M = \omega J \text{ joules sec/rad} = \text{inertia power/unit acceleration}$$

$$= \text{angular momentum,} \quad \text{(also W/mech rad/sec}^2)$$

$$m = \text{number of phases;} \quad VI_{sc} = \frac{VE}{X_s} \text{ in per phase terms}$$

In per unit notation,

$$\frac{\partial P}{\partial\delta} = \frac{VE}{X}(\cos\delta)\,\theta$$

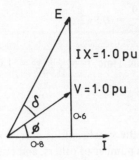

Fig. 35

$$\omega = \text{synchronous speed in rad/sec}$$

With the given data, Fig. 35

$$\tan(\delta + \phi) = \frac{1.6}{0.8} = 2.0 \quad \text{and} \quad (\delta + \phi) = 63.43°$$

$$\text{Load phase angle}, \phi = \cos^{-1} 0.8 = 36.87°$$

Then,

$$\delta = 63.43 - 36.87 = 26.56°$$

Now,

$$E \cos(\delta + \phi) = 0.8 \text{ p.u.}$$

∴

$$E = \frac{0.8}{0.447} = 1.79 \text{ p.u.}$$

$\dfrac{\partial P}{\partial \delta}$ at load angle $\delta = 26.56°$ for $1°$ mech displacement

$$= \frac{1.0 \times 1.79}{1.0} \cos 26.56° \times \frac{2\pi}{180}$$

$$= 1.79 \times 0.895 \times 0.0349 = 0.056 \text{ p.u.}$$

$$= 3.36 \text{ MW/}°\text{mech}$$

$$= 3.36 \times 57.29 = 192.5 \text{ MW/mech rad} = P_{syn}$$

$$M = J \times \frac{2\pi N}{60} = \frac{35\,000 \times 2\pi \times 1500}{60}$$

$$= 5497.8 \times 10^3 \text{ W/mech rad/sec}$$

Hence

$$\omega_0 = \sqrt{\frac{P_{syn}}{M}} = \sqrt{\frac{192.5 \times 10^6}{5497.8 \times 10^3}} = \sqrt{35}$$

$$= 5.9 \text{ rad/sec}$$

$$f_0 = \frac{5.9}{2\pi} = 0.942$$

$$\text{Periodic Time}, t = \frac{1}{0.942} = 1.06 \text{ sec}$$

Example 36

Evolve an expression for the synchronising torque of an unloaded alternator running in parallel with a number of others, and evaluate the expression for a displacement of 1 mechanical degree in a 3-phase 6-pole 50 Hz 5000 kVA machine with 20% reactance.

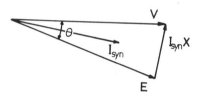

Fig. 36

Solution   (Ref. 7, p. 54; Ref. 2, p. 195)

Under unloaded synchronous conditions,

$$\text{machine emf}, E = \text{bus-bar voltage}, V$$

With a displacement of θ elect rad, and resistance neglected, the phasor diagram/phase will be as shown in Fig. 36. Then

$$I_{syn}X = 2E \sin \theta/2$$

and

$$I_{syn} = \frac{2E \sin \theta/2}{X} = 2I_{sc} \sin \theta/2, \quad \text{where} \quad I_{sc} = \frac{E}{X}$$

$$\text{Synchronising Power}, P_{syn} = mEI_{syn} \cos \theta/2$$

$$= mE(2I_{sc} \sin \theta/2) \cos \theta/2$$

$$= mEI_{sc} \sin \theta$$

$$\hat{=} mEI_{sc}\theta$$

where θ is small, and $m = $ phases,

$$= 2\pi n \textcircled{T}_{syn}$$

where n = rev/sec.

$$\text{Synchronising Torque, } (T)_{syn} = \frac{mEI_{sc}\theta}{2\pi n} \text{ newton metre}$$

This may be written,

$$(T)_{syn} = \frac{mEI(I_{sc}/I)\theta}{2\pi n} = \frac{(kVA)(k)\theta \times 10^3}{2\pi n} \text{ newton metre}$$

where k = s.c. ratio = $I_{sc}/I = E/IX$, and I = rated F.L. current

$$\left[
\begin{array}{l}
\text{Expressed in f.p.s. units:} \\[2mm]
\qquad (T)_{syn} = \frac{mEI_{sc}\theta\,33\,000}{746 \times 2\pi N} = 7040\frac{(kVA)(k)\theta}{N} \text{ lb ft}
\end{array}
\right]$$

where N = rpm

Numerical part

$$\text{Displacement, } \theta \text{ in elect degrees} = p\psi$$

where ψ = displacement in mech degrees.

Now, pairs of poles, $p = 3$

$$\text{Displacement, } 1°\text{mech} = 3°\text{elect} = \frac{\pi}{180} \times 3 = 0.0524 \text{ elect rad}$$

$$n = 1000/60 \text{ rev/sec}$$

Hence,

$$
\begin{aligned}
(T)_{syn} &= \frac{mEI_{sc}\theta}{2\pi n} = \frac{(kVA)(k)\theta \times 10^3}{2\pi n} \\[2mm]
&= \frac{5000 \times 5 \times 0.0524 \times 60 \times 10^3}{2\pi \times 1000} \\[2mm]
&= 12\,510 \text{ newton metre}
\end{aligned}
$$

$$\left[
\begin{array}{l}
\text{In f.p.s. units;} \\[2mm]
\qquad (T)_{syn} = \frac{550 \times 12\,510}{746} = 9223 \text{ lb ft}
\end{array}
\right]$$

Example 37

A 6600 V, 3000 kVA 50 Hz 6-pole 3-phase Y-connected alternator is running in parallel with a number of others on the same bus-bars. Calculate the synchronising power and torque per mechanical degree of displacement:

(a) unloaded and normally excited, and

(b) on full load and over-excited to produce a power factor of 0.9 lagging. The synchronous impedance of the machine is $(0.3 + j4)$ ohm/phase.

Evolve any formula used for the synchronising power or torque.

Solution

Last part: The power/angle relationship for the loaded synchronous generator, including stator resistance, can be stated, (Ref. 2, p. 169); Working per phase,

$$\text{Power input}, P_i = \frac{VE}{Z} \sin (\delta - \alpha) + \frac{E^2}{Z} \sin \alpha$$

$$= VI_{sc} \sin (\delta - \alpha) + EI_{sc} \sin \alpha$$

where $\alpha = \tan^{-1} R/X$.

If a displacement, θ elect rad occurs,

$$P_i' = VI_{sc} \sin (\delta - \alpha - \theta) + EI_{sc} \sin \alpha$$

$$\text{Synchronising Power}, P_{syn} = P_i - P_i'$$

$$= VI_{sc}[\sin (\delta - \alpha) - \sin (\delta - \alpha - \theta)]$$

$$= VI_{sc}\{\sin (\delta - \alpha)[1 - \cos \theta] + \cos (\delta - \alpha) \sin \theta\}$$

$$= VI_{sc}\{\sin (\delta - \alpha)[2 \sin^2 \theta/2] + \cos (\delta - \alpha) \sin \theta\}$$

$$= VI_{sc}\{2 \sin (\delta - \alpha) \sin^2 \theta/2 + \cos (\delta - \alpha) \sin \theta\}$$

Assuming that θ is small, the first term is negligible. Then

$$P_{syn} = VI_{sc} \cos (\delta - \alpha) \sin \theta$$

$$\backsimeq VI_{sc} \cos (\delta - \alpha)\theta \backsimeq VI_{sc}\theta \cos \delta \text{ watt/phase},$$

assuming α and θ are small.

$$\text{Syn. Torque}, ⓉÃ_{syn} = \frac{\text{syn power}}{2\pi n} = \frac{mVI_{sc}\theta \cos \delta}{2\pi n} \text{ newton metre}$$

This may be written:

$$Ⓣ_{syn} = \frac{mVI(I_{sc}/I)\theta \cos \delta}{2\pi n}$$

$$= \frac{(kVA)(k)\theta \cos \delta \times 10^3}{2\pi n} \text{ newton metre}$$

where $k = $ s.c. ratio $= I_{sc}/I = E/IZ$ and $I = $ F.L. rated current.

$$\left[\begin{array}{l} \text{Expressed in f.p.s. units;} \\ \qquad \textcircled{T}_{\text{syn}} = \dfrac{550}{746} (\textcircled{T}_{\text{syn}} \text{ in m.k.s. units) lb ft} \end{array}\right]$$

Part (a)

$$Z = (0.3 + j4) \quad \text{and} \quad |Z| = 4.012 \text{ ohm}$$

With normal Y-connection,

$$V = \frac{6600}{\sqrt{3}} = 3810 \text{ volt} = E$$

$$\theta = 1^\circ \text{mech} = 3^\circ \text{elect} = 3\pi/180 \text{ elect rad}$$

$$P_{\text{syn}} = V I_{sc} \theta \cos \delta \quad (\text{unloaded}, \cos \delta = 1.0 \text{ since } \delta = 0)$$

$$= \frac{3810 \times 3810 \times 3\pi}{4.012 \times 180} = 189\,400 \text{ watt/phase}$$

$$\text{Syn. Power} = 568.2 \text{ kW for 3 phases}$$

$$\text{Syn. Torque} = \frac{568.2 \times 10^3}{2\pi n} = \frac{568.2 \times 10^3 \times 60}{2\pi \times 1000}$$

$$= 5426 \text{ newton metre}$$

$$\left[\text{In f.p.s. units, } \textcircled{T}_{\text{syn}} = \frac{550}{746} (5426) = 4000 \text{ lb ft} \right]$$

Part (b)

$$\text{Rated full-load current} = \frac{3000 \times 10^3}{\sqrt{3} \times 6600} = 262.5 \text{ amp}$$

Working per phase, and with current as phasor of reference, (Fig. 37)

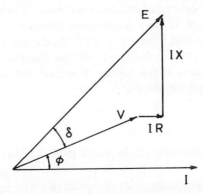

Fig. 37

$$E = V(\cos \phi + j \sin \phi) + IR + jIX$$
$$= 3810(0.9 + j0.4357) + 262.5(0.3 + j4)$$
$$= 3429 + j1660 + 78.75 + j1050$$
$$= 3508 + j2710 = 4428 \underline{/37°36'}$$

Now

$$\phi = \cos^{-1}0.9 = 25°50' \quad \text{and} \quad \delta = 37°36' - 25°50' = 11°46'$$

Hence for a displacement $\theta = 3°$elect, and using approx,

$$P_{syn} = VI_s\theta \cos \delta$$
$$= \frac{3810 \times 4428 \times \sin 3° \times \cos 11°46'}{4.012}$$
$$= \frac{3810 \times 4428 \times 0.0523 \times 0.9790}{4.012} = 215\,400\,\text{W/ph}$$

$$P_{syn} \text{ for 3 phases} = 646.2 \text{ kW}$$

$$\text{(T)}_{syn} = \frac{646.2 \times 10^3}{2\pi n} = \frac{646.2 \times 10^3 \times 60}{2\pi \times 1000} = 6170 \text{ newton metre}$$

$$\left[\text{In f.p.s. units;} \right.$$
$$\left. \text{(T)}_{syn} = \frac{550}{746}(6170) = 4550 \text{ lb ft} \right]$$

Example 38

A 3-phase 2200 V Y-connected alternator is connected to bus-bars of constant frequency and voltage. It has a synchronous impedance of $(0.5 + j10)$ ohm/phase. When the induced voltage is 2500 V, the alternator has a power factor of unity. The excitation is decreased, without changing the driving torque, until the power factor is 0.8 leading. Calculate the induced voltage and current under the new conditions.

Solution

The power/angle relationship can be stated, (Ref. 2, p. 169)

$$\text{Input power/phase} = P_i = \frac{VE}{Z} \sin (\delta - \alpha) + \frac{E^2}{Z} \sin \alpha$$

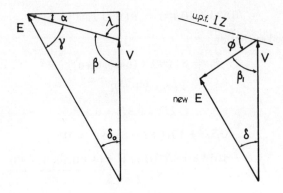

Fig. 38(a) and (b)

$$= \text{a constant for constant torque and speed}$$

$$V = \frac{2200}{\sqrt{3}} = 1271 \text{ volt/phase}$$

$$Z = (0.5 + j10) \quad \text{and} \quad |Z| \triangleq 10 \text{ ohm}$$

At $\cos \phi = 1.0$,

$$E = \frac{2500}{\sqrt{3}} = 1443 \text{ volt/phase}$$

Unity power factor phasor diagram is shown schematically in Fig. 38(a).

$$\tan \alpha = 0.5/10 \qquad \therefore \ \alpha = 2°52'$$

$$\lambda = (90° - \alpha) = 87°8'$$

$$\beta = (180° - \lambda) = 92°52'$$

Now

$$\frac{E}{\sin \beta} = \frac{V}{\sin \gamma}$$

$\therefore$

$$\sin \gamma = \frac{V \sin \beta}{E} = \frac{1271 \times 0.9987}{1443} = 0.8794$$

$$\gamma = 61°36'$$

Then

$$\delta_0 = (180° - \beta - \gamma) = 25°32'$$

$$P_i = \frac{1271 \times 1443}{10} \sin 22°40' + \frac{(1443)^2}{10} \sin 2°52'$$

$$= \frac{1271 \times 1443 \times 0.385}{10} + \frac{(1443)^2 \times 0.05}{10}$$

$$= 70\,690 + 10\,400 = 81\,090 \text{ watt/phase}$$

With decreased excitation,

$$P_i = 81\,090 \quad \text{(unchanged)}$$
$$= VI \cos \phi + I^2 R$$
$$= (1271 \times 0.8I) + 0.5I^2$$
$$0.5I^2 + 1016.8I - 81\,090 = 0$$
$$\text{New } I = \frac{-1016.8 \pm \sqrt{(1016.8)^2 + (4 \times 0.5 \times 81\,090)}}{2 \times 0.5}$$
$$= -1016.8 \pm \sqrt{1.034 \times 10^6 + 0.1622 \times 10^6}$$
$$= -1016.8 \pm \sqrt{1.196 \times 10^6}$$
$$= -1016.8 + 1093$$
$$= 76 \text{ amp}$$

$$\text{New } IZ = 760 \text{ volt}$$

At 0.8 p.f. leading, $\phi = 36°56'$ and β becomes $\beta_1 = (\beta - \phi)$ (Fig. 38(b))

$$\beta_1 = (92°52' - 36°56') = 55°56'$$
$$E^2 = V^2 + (IZ)^2 - 2V(IZ) \cos \beta_1$$
$$= (1271)^2 + (760)^2 - 2(1271)(760)(0.561)$$
$$= 1.615 \times 10^6 + 0.5776 \times 10^6 - 1.083 \times 10^6$$
$$= 1.109 \times 10^6$$

$$\text{New } E = 1053 \text{ volt/phase}$$

Example 39

A 3-phase synchronous generator operates on constant voltage, constant frequency busbars and has a constant driving torque. Show that the locus of the E-phasor lies on a circle of radius,

$$\left[\frac{P_i Z}{\sin \alpha} + \left(\frac{V}{2 \sin \alpha} \right)^2 \right]^{1/2}$$

where $P_i =$ input power and $\alpha = \tan^{-1} R/X$ in conventional notation.

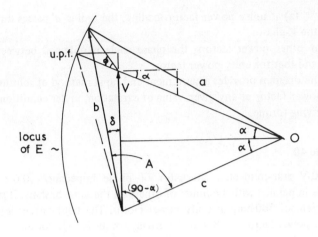

Fig. 39

Solution   (Ref. 2, p. 172; Ref. 4, p. 374)

The power/angle relationship can be stated,

$$P_i = \frac{VE}{Z} \sin(\delta - \alpha) + \frac{E^2}{Z} \sin \alpha$$

= constant for constant torque and speed

Then,

$$\frac{P_i Z}{\sin \alpha} = \frac{VE \sin(\delta - \alpha)}{\sin \alpha} + E^2$$

$$\frac{P_i Z}{\sin \alpha} + \left(\frac{V}{2 \sin \alpha}\right)^2 = \frac{VE \sin(\delta - \alpha)}{\sin \alpha} + E^2 + \left(\frac{V}{2 \sin \alpha}\right)^2$$

This equation can be expressed simply,

$$a^2 = -2bc \cos A + b^2 + c^2$$

which is an equation for a triangle of sides a, b and c, with a and c constants.

$$2bc = \frac{VE}{\sin \alpha}$$

and thus

$$\cos A = -\sin(\delta - \alpha) = \sin(\alpha - \delta)$$

and

$$A = (90° - \alpha + \delta) \quad \text{and varies with } \delta.$$

These dimensions are related to the phasor diagram as shown in Fig. 39 and the locus of E is determined.

Notes: (a) at unity power factor loading, the radius 'a' passes through the end of the *V*-phasor,

(b) at other power factors, the phase angle is obtained between the *IZ* phasor and that for unity power factor,

(c) the diagram provides a convenient and rapid method of solution for *IZ*, *I* and power factor at any given value of excitation, under conditions of constant driving torque.

Example 40

A 6600-V star-connected alternator of phase impedance $(0.6 + j3)$ ohm operates in parallel with a number of others on the same busbars. It supplies a line current of 300 amp at unity power factor. The field current is increased until the power factor is 0.8, but the driving torque is kept constant. Calculate the new value of current. Check the solution by an independent graphical method.

Solution

$$V_p = \frac{6600}{\sqrt{3}} = 3810 \text{ volt}$$

$$P_0 = VI \cos \phi$$

$$= 3810 \times 300 \times 1.0 = 1143 \text{ kW}$$

$$P_i = VI \cos \phi + I^2 R$$

$$= 1143 \times 10^3 + 0.6(300)^2$$

$$= 1143 \times 10^3 + 54 \times 10^3 = 1197 \times 10^3 \text{ watt}$$

At new p.f. = 0.8; (lagging for over-excitation)

$$P_i = 1197 \times 10^3 \text{ watt} \quad \text{(unchanged)}$$

$$= VI \cos \phi + I^2 R$$

$$= 3810 \times 0.8 \times I + 0.6I^2$$

$$0.6I^2 + 3048I - 1197 \times 10^3 = 0$$

$$\therefore \quad \text{new } I = \frac{-3048 \pm \sqrt{[(3048)^2 + (4 \times 0.6 \times 1197 \times 10^3)]}}{2 \times 0.6}$$

$$= \frac{-3048 \pm \sqrt{[9.29 \times 10^6 + 2.87 \times 10^6]}}{1.2}$$

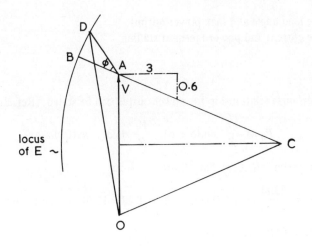

Fig. 40

$$= \frac{-3048 \pm 3485}{1.2} = 364 \text{ amp}$$

Graphical solution: The method described in Example 39 applies. Now

$$Z = (0.6 + j3) \quad \text{and} \quad |Z| = 3.06 \text{ ohm}$$

At unity power factor,
$$IZ = 300 \times 3.06 = 918 \text{ volt}$$

Choose a volt scale, say 1 cm = 1000 volt. Draw $V = 3810$ volt = 3.81 cm = OA vertically, Fig. 40. Draw $\perp$ bisector of V. At A draw a line at $\alpha = \tan^{-1}$ 0.6/3 (3 arbitrary units horizontal, 0.6 arbitrary units vertical), to meet $\perp$ bisector at C. Produce CA a distance $AB = IZ = 918$ volt = 0.918 cm.

With centre C and radius CB describe an arc, which is the locus of E. Then draw AD at ϕ ($= \cos^{-1} 0.8$) to AB. Now

$$AD = \text{new } IZ = 1.12 \text{ cm} = 1120 \text{ volt}$$

Hence,
$$\text{new } I = \frac{\text{new } IZ}{Z} = \frac{1120}{3.06} = 364 \text{ amp}$$

Example 41

A 3-phase 2200 V 50 Hz Y-connected alternator, running in parallel with a number of others, has a synchronous impedance of $(0.8 + j6)$ ohm/phase. The excitation is adjusted to 1.23 per unit. Calculate:

(a) the maximum power output,

(b) the load angle at $\frac{1}{3}$ max power output,

(c) the current and power factor at stalling.

Solution

The power/angle relationship for power output can be stated, (Ref. 2, p. 170)

$$P_0 = \frac{VE}{Z} \sin(\delta + \alpha) - \frac{V^2}{Z} \sin \alpha \quad \text{watt/phase}$$

where

$$\alpha = \tan^{-1} R/X = \tan^{-1} 0.8/6 = 7°36'$$

$$V = \frac{2200}{\sqrt{3}} = 1270 \text{ volt}; \quad E = 1.23 \times 1270 = 1562 \text{ volt}$$

$$Z = (0.8 + j6) \quad \text{and} \quad |Z| = 6.05 \text{ ohm}$$

Part (a). P_0 is maximum when $\sin(\delta + \alpha) = 1.0$

$$P_{0_{max}} = \frac{VE}{Z} - \frac{V^2}{Z} \sin \alpha$$

$$= \frac{1270 \times 1562}{6.05} - \frac{(1270)^2 \times 0.8}{6.05 \times 6.05}$$

$$= 328 \times 10^3 - 35.2 \times 10^3 = 292.8 \text{ kW/phase}$$

Part (b).   At

$$\tfrac{1}{3}P_{0_{max}} = 97.6 \times 10^3 \text{ watt/phase}$$

we substitute,

$$97.6 \times 10^3 = 328 \times 10^3 \sin(\delta + 7°36') - 35.2 \times 10^3$$

$$\sin(\delta + 7°36') = \frac{132.8}{328} = 0.405$$

$$(\delta + 7°36') = 23°54'$$

$$\delta = 16°18'$$

Part (c).   At stalling, i.e., at $P_{0_{max}}$, then $(\delta + \alpha) = 90°$ and

$$\delta_{max} = (90° - 7°36') = 82°24'$$

From the phasor diagram, Fig. 41

$$(IZ)^2 = V^2 + E^2 - 2VE \cos \delta$$

$$= (1270)^2 + (1562)^2 - 2(1270)(1562)(0.132)$$

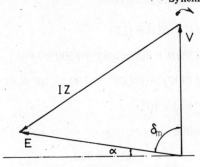

Fig. 41

$$= 161.3 \times 10^4 + 244.1 \times 10^4 - 52.5 \times 10^4$$

$$= 352.9 \times 10^4$$

$$IZ = 1878$$

$$I = \frac{1878}{6.05} = 310.5 \text{ amp}$$

Now $P_0 = VI \cos \phi = 292.8$ kW at stalling. Then

$$\cos \phi = \frac{292.8 \times 10^3}{1270 \times 310.5} = 0.743$$

and

$$\phi = 42° \quad \text{leading}$$

Example 42

A 6600 V Y-connected alternator, with synchronous impedance of $(0.6 + j3)$ ohm/phase, delivers 300 amp at unity power factor to constant 6600 V bus-bars. Calculate:

(a) the load angle,

(b) the new load angle, current and power factor if the excitation is reduced by 20% but the power output is maintained constant,

(c) the maximum power output at the new excitation.

Solution

$$\text{phase voltage, } V = \frac{6600}{\sqrt{3}} = 3810 \text{ volt}$$

Part (a). $I_p = I_L = 300$ amp at unity power factor.

From the phasor diagram, Fig. 42

$$E^2 = (V + IR)^2 + (IX)^2$$
$$= (3810 + 300 \times 0.6)^2 + (300 \times 3)^2$$
$$= (3990)^2 + (900)^2 = 1592 \times 10^4 + 81 \times 10^4$$
$$= 1673 \times 10^4$$
$$E = 4090 \text{ volt}$$

$$\sin \delta = \frac{IX}{E} = \frac{900}{4090} = 0.22$$

$\therefore$
$$\delta = 12°43'$$

Part (b)

$$P_0 = VI \cos \phi = 3810 \times 300 \times 1.0 = 1143 \times 10^3 \text{ watt/phase}$$
$$= \frac{VE}{Z} \sin (\delta + \alpha) - \frac{V^2}{Z} \sin \alpha$$

Now
$$Z = (0.6 + j3) \quad \text{and} \quad |Z| = 3.06 \text{ ohm}$$
$$\alpha = \tan^{-1} R/X = \tan^{-1} 0.2 = 11°18'$$

New $E = 0.8 \times 4090 = 3272$ volt

Then,
$$P_0 = \frac{3810 \times 3272}{3.06} \sin (\delta + \alpha) - \frac{(3810)^2}{3.06} \sin \alpha$$
$$= 4074 \times 10^3 \sin (\delta + 11°18') - 929 \times 10^3$$

which must equal 1143×10^3 watt/phase, (unchanged).

$$\sin (\delta + 11°18') = \frac{1143 \times 10^3 + 929 \times 10^3}{4074 \times 10^3} = 0.5087$$
$$(\delta + 11°18') = 30°35'$$
$$\text{New } \delta = 19°17'$$

Applying the cosine rule, (Fig. 42),

$$(IZ)^2 = V^2 + E^2 - 2VE \cos \delta$$
$$= (3810)^2 + (3272)^2 - 2(3810)(3272)(0.944)$$
$$= 1460 \times 10^4 + 1070 \times 10^4 - 2358 \times 10^4$$
$$= 172 \times 10^4$$
$$IZ = 1311 \text{ volt}$$

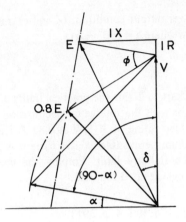

Fig. 42

$$\text{New } I = \frac{1311}{3.06} = 428.5 \text{ amp}$$

Now

$$\text{unchanged } P_0 = VI \cos \phi = 1143 \times 10^3 \text{ watt/phase}$$

∴

$$\text{New } \cos \phi = \frac{1143 \times 10^3}{3810 \times 428.5} = 0.7 \quad \text{leading}$$

$$\text{New } \phi = 45°37' \quad \text{leading}$$

Part (c). Maximum P_0 occurs when $(\delta + \alpha) = 90°$. Then

$$\text{Max } P_0 = \frac{VE}{Z} - \frac{V^2}{Z} \sin \alpha$$

$$= \frac{(3810)(3272)}{3.06} - \frac{(3810)^2 \times 0.6}{3.06 \times 3.06}$$

$$= 4074 \times 10^3 - 929 \times 10^3$$

$$= 3145 \text{ kW/phase}$$

Graphical solution: Choose a voltage scale and draw the u.p.f. phasor diagram, Fig. 42. Now u.p.f. IZ, say $I_0 Z = IZ \cos \phi \propto VI \cos \phi = P_0$, since V and Z are both constants. Hence for a constant P_0, $I_0 Z$ is a constant and the locus of the E-phasor is the line perpendicular to $I_0 Z$. Draw this locus. (*N.B.* I_0 signifies unity p.f. current.)

Describe an arc = 0.8E to intersect the E-locus. This determines the new E-phasor. Join the intersection to the end of the V-phasor. This determines new IZ. New ϕ is obtained between $I_0 Z$ and the new IZ.

At maximum power output condition, IZ and ϕ are obtained by swinging new E to the position where $\delta = (90° - \alpha)$.

Example 43

Construct a Power Chart to define the practical limits of stable operation of a synchronous generator with the following specification: 11 kV, 3 phase star-connected with full load rating of 30 MW at 0.8 p.f. The short circuit ratio is 0.642 and the maximum permissible exciter current is 2.4 p.u. Allow a 10% power margin on the stability limit. Employ the chart to determine the excitation and load angle at rated full load.

Solution.   (Ref. 2, p. 175; Ref. 4, p. 391)

The Power Chart is based on the phasor diagram and in simplest form, resistance is neglected. Now

$$\text{phase voltage, } V = \frac{11\,000}{\sqrt{3}} = 6350 \text{ volt}$$

$$\text{S.C.R.} = 0.642 = I_{sc}/I = V/IX_s \quad \text{where } I = \text{rated F.L.}$$

$$I = \frac{30 \times 10^6}{3 \times 6350 \times 0.8} = 1967 \text{ amp}$$

$$\therefore \qquad X_s = \frac{6350}{1967 \times 0.642} = 5.0 \text{ ohm}$$

Referring to Fig. 43 choose volt scale, 1 cm = 1000 volt. Then

$$\text{current scale is 1 cm} = \frac{1000}{X_s} = 200 \text{ amp}$$

$$\text{VA/phase scale, 1 cm} = \text{phase volts} \times \text{current scale}$$

$$= 6350 \times 200 = 1270 \text{ kVA/phase}$$

This is commonly scaled for 3 phases;
    Then 3-phase VA scale, 1 cm = 3.81 MVA.
    Draw $\overline{AO}$ = phase volts = 6350 = 6.35 cm.
    Extend $\overline{AO}$ to D, where $\overline{AD}$ = 2.4 × 6350 volts = 15.24 cm.
    Erect a perpendicular at O and scale MVA along $\overline{OP}$ and $\overline{OD}$ to accommodate machine MVA $= \dfrac{30}{0.8} = 37.5$ MVA.
    Draw a horizontal at rated MW = 30 MW on $\overline{OP}$, to meet an arc of radius 37.5 MVA at point B.

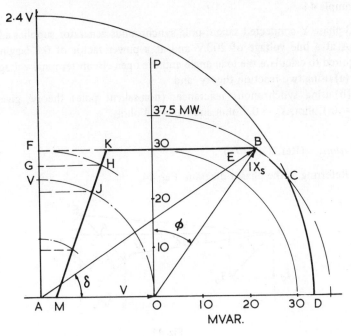

Fig. 43

Describe an arc of radius $\overline{OD} = 2.4\,V = 15.24$ cm and $\overline{CD}$ is the limit imposed by rotor heating.

Now theoretical stability limit for the rated load occurs at F, when $\delta = 90°$. Allow a 10% margin $= 3\,MW = \overline{FG}$. Project G to the correct excitation circle at H. Further points are obtained at, say J, corresponding to p.u. excitation. Hence the practical limits of stable operation are determined within the curve MKBCD.

Last part.   At full rated load;
     Draw IX_s at ϕ ($= \cos^{-1} 0.8$) to $\overline{OP}$ giving $\overline{OB}$. Join $\overline{AB}$.
     Measure $\overline{AB} = E = 14.55$ cm $= 14\,550$ volt.

$$\underline{/BAO} = \delta = 33.0°$$

Check:

$$P/\text{phase} = \frac{VE}{X_s} \sin \delta = 10\,MW$$

$$\sin \delta = \frac{10 \times 10^6 \times 5}{6350 \times 14\,550} = 0.542$$

$$\delta = 32.8°$$

Example 44

A 3-phase Y-connected salient-pole synchronous generator supplies a load of 58 A at a line voltage of 200 V and at a power factor of 0.8 lagging. It is required to calculate the load angle and the open-circuit terminal voltage:

(a) using two-reaction theory, and

(b) using synchronous reactance, (non-salient pole) theory, given that $R_a = 0.1$ ohm, $X_d = 0.7$ ohm and $X_q = 0.4$ ohm.

Solution.   (Ref. 2, p. 178)

(a) Referring to the phasor diagram, Fig. 44

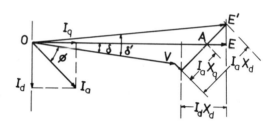

Fig. 44

$$V/\text{phase} = \frac{200}{\sqrt{3}} = 115.47 \text{ volt} = (V + j0)$$

$$OA\underline{/\delta} = (V + j0) + (I_a\underline{/-\phi})R_a + (I_a\underline{/-\phi})jX_q$$

$$= 115.47 + 58(0.8 - j0.6)(0.1) + 58(0.8 - j0.6)(j0.4)$$

$$= 134.03 + j15.08$$

$$\delta = \tan^{-1}\frac{15.08}{134.03} = 6.42°$$

Now

$$(\delta + \phi) = (6.42 + 36.87) = 43.29°$$

$$I_d = I_a \sin(\delta + \phi) = 58 \times 0.686 = 39.79 \text{ A}$$

$$I_q = I_a \cos(\delta + \phi) = 58 \times 0.728 = 42.22 \text{ A}$$

O.C. terminal volts/phase $= E = V \cos \delta + I_q R_a + I_d X_d$

$$= 114.78 + 4.22 + 27.85$$

$$= 146.85 \text{ volt}$$

O.C. terminal volts, (line) $= \sqrt{3} \times 146.85 = 254.35 \text{ volt}$

(b) Using non-salient pole theory,

Synchronous reactance $X_s = X_d$

$$E_{ph} = V\underline{/0^\circ} + (I\underline{/-\phi})(R_a + jX_s)$$

$$= 115.47 + 58(0.8 - j0.6)(0.1 + j0.7)$$

$$= 144.47 + j29.0$$

$$= 147.35\underline{/11.35^\circ}$$

$$E_{line} = \sqrt{3} \times 147.35 = 255.21 \text{ volt}$$

$$\delta = 11.35^\circ$$

Note the small error in using synchronous reactance theory for a salient-pole machine in respect of voltage prediction, but an appreciable error in the prediction of load angle, δ.

Example 45

A 3-phase synchronous generator operating at 0.6 per unit load is connected to the Grid through an interconnector such that the power/angle curve is $P = 1.3 \sin \delta$. A 3-phase fault occurs on the interconnector which causes the machine to operate on a power/angle relationship, $P_1 = 0.1 \sin \delta$ until the fault is cleared. When the system is restored the machine reverts to the condition $P = 1.3 \sin \delta$.

It is required to determine the critical clearing angle for transient stability.

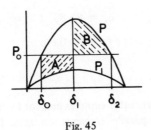

Fig. 45

Solution. (Ref. 7, p. 270; Ref. 2, p. 197)

The condition required is termed 'the equal area criterion'. Referring to Fig. 45

$$P_0 = 0.6 \text{ p.u.} = 1.3 \sin \delta_0$$

$\therefore$ $$\delta_0 = \sin^{-1} \frac{0.6}{1.3} = 27.49° = 0.48 \text{ rad}$$

$$\delta_2 = 180° - \sin^{-1}\left(\frac{P_0}{P}\right) = 180° - \delta_0 = 152.51°$$

$$= 2.66 \text{ rad}$$

The criterion requires Area A = Area B, or

$$\int_{\delta_0}^{\delta_1} (P_0 - P_1 \sin \delta) \, d\delta + \int_{\delta_1}^{\delta_2} (P_0 - P \sin \delta) \, d\delta = 0$$

$$[P_0\delta + P_1 \cos \delta]_{\delta_0}^{\delta_1} + [P_0\delta + P \cos \delta]_{\delta_1}^{\delta_2} = 0$$

$$P_0\delta_1 + P_1 \cos \delta_1 - P_0\delta_0 - P_1 \cos \delta_0 + P_0\delta_2 + P \cos \delta_2 - P_0\delta_1 - P \cos \delta_1 = 0$$

Collecting terms,

$$\cos \delta_1 = \frac{P_0(\delta_0 - \delta_2) + P_1 \cos \delta_0 - P \cos \delta_2}{(P_1 - P)}$$

Substituting numerical values,

$$\cos \delta_1 = \frac{0.6(0.48 - 2.66) + 0.1 \cos 27.49° - 1.3 \cos 152.51°}{(0.1 - 1.3)}$$

$$= \frac{-1.308 + 0.1 \times 0.887 - 1.3(-0.887)}{-1.2}$$

$$= \frac{-0.0662}{-1.2} = 0.0552$$

$\therefore$ $$\delta_1 = 86.83°$$

This is the critical clearing angle for $P_0 = 0.6$ p.u.

Example 46

A 3-phase synchronous generator supplies current to constant 1.0 p.u. voltage busbars via two identical parallel transmission lines. The sending end and the receiving end of the lines are each connected via a transformer, to the generator and to the infinite busbars respectively (see Fig. 46). The system constants are per unit values based on the kVA rating of the generator, as follows; Generator; $X_d = 1.0$, $X_d' = 0.35$, $X_d'' = 0.25$, $T_d' = 1.8$ sec, $T_d'' = 0.04$ sec. Line $X_1 = 0.5$. Each transformer $X_t = 0.1$. A steady loading on the generator is 0.8 of the kVA rating, due to a unity power factor load on the busbars.

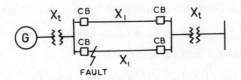

Fig. 46

A solid 3-phase short circuit occurs at the sending end of one transmission line. For these conditions, calculate

(a) the largest possible initial rms total fault current in one phase,

(b) the symmetrical time-dependent generator short-circuit current,

(c) Given that the sending-end circuit breaker of the faulted line opens after 0.15 sec, calculate the fault current per phase which has to be interrupted. Assume the d.c. and subtransient components are negligible at this time.

Solution

Effective reactance between generator and the steady load,

$$X_e = 2X_t + \left(\frac{X_1^2}{2X_1}\right) = 0.2 + \left(\frac{0.5 \times 0.5}{0.5 + 0.5}\right)$$

$$= 0.2 + 0.25 = 0.45$$

(a) Prefault voltage behind X_d'',

$$E'' = E_b + I[j(X_d'' + X_e)]$$

$$= 1.00 + 0.8[j(0.25 + 0.45)]$$

$$= 1.00 + j0.56 = (1 + 0.31)^{1/2}/\tan^{-1} 0.56$$

$$= 1.14 \underline{/29.2^\circ}$$

Initial symmetrical I'' to fault, from generator and from busbars

$$= I_G'' + I_{BB}$$

$$= \frac{E''}{X_d'' + X_t} + \frac{E_b}{X_t + (X_1^2/2X_1)}$$

$$= \frac{1.14}{0.25 + 0.1} + \frac{1.00}{0.10 + 0.25}$$

$$= 3.26 + 2.86 = 6.12 \text{ p.u.}$$

Maximum asymmetry occurs when d.c. component = peak a.c.

∴   d.c. componnent in fault $=$ peak a.c. component

$$= \sqrt{2} \times 6.12 = 8.65 \text{ p.u.}$$

Then largest rms total fault current/phase

$$= (I_{ac}^2 + I_{dc}^2)^{1/2} = (6.12^2 + 8.65^2)^{1/2}$$

$$= 10.60 \text{ p.u.}$$

(b) Prefault voltage behind X_d',

$$E' = E_b + I[j(X_d' + X_e)]$$

$$= 1.00 + 0.8[j(0.35 + 0.45)]$$

$$= 1.00 + j0.64 = (1 + 0.41)^{1/2} / \tan^{-1} 0.64$$

$$= 1.19 \underline{/32.6°}$$

Initial symmetrical I' from generator to fault,

$$I' = \frac{E'}{X_d' + X_t} = \frac{1.19}{0.35 + 0.1} = 2.64 \text{ p.u.}$$

Prefault voltage behind X_d,

$$E = E_b + I[j(X_d + X_e)]$$

$$= 1.00 + 0.8[j(1.00 + 0.45)]$$

$$= 1.00 + j1.16 = (1 + 1.35)^{1/2} / \tan^{-1} 1.16$$

$$= 1.53 \underline{/49.2°}$$

Steady-state final I, from generator to fault,

$$I = \frac{E}{X_d + X_t} = \frac{1.53}{(1.00 + 0.1)} = 1.39 \text{ p.u.}$$

The symmetrical generator current during the Transient period is governed by a time constant, T_d', which is adjusted for the external reactance to the fault, (in this case transformer X_t), and is given, (Ref. 16),

$$T_{de}' = T_d' \left(\frac{X_d}{X_d'}\right)\left(\frac{X_d' + X_t}{X_d + X_t}\right)$$

$$= 1.8 \left(\frac{1.0}{0.35}\right)\left(\frac{0.35 + 0.1}{1.0 + 0.1}\right) = 1.8(2.86)(1.23)$$

$$= 6.33 \text{ sec}$$

Similarly, an approx. adjustment of T_d'' may be made,

$$T''_{de} = T''_d \left(\frac{X'_d}{X''_d}\right) \left(\frac{X''_d + X_t}{X'_d + X_t}\right)$$

$$= 0.04 \left(\frac{0.35}{0.25}\right)\left(\frac{0.25 + 0.1}{0.35 + 0.1}\right) = 0.04(1.4)(0.78)$$

$$= 0.0437 \text{ sec}$$

∴   Time dependent s.c. symmetrical $I_{\text{generator}}$

$$= I + (I' - I)e^{-t/T'_{de}} + (I'' - I')e^{-t/T''_{de}}$$

$$= 1.39 + (2.64 - 1.39)e^{-t/6.33} + (3.26 - 2.64)e^{-t/0.0437}$$

$$= 1.39 + 1.25\,e^{-0.158t} + 0.62\,e^{-22.88t} \text{ per unit}$$

(c) At 0.15 sec, (neglecting subtransient and d.c. components). From the generator,

$$I_{sc} = 1.39 + 1.25\,e^{-0.024}$$

$$= 1.39 + 0.977$$

$$= 2.37 \text{ p.u.}$$

One half the current from Inf. busbars passes through the circuit breaker = 2.86/2 = 1.43 p.u.

∴   Total symmetrical current in circuit breaker

$$= 2.37 + 1.43$$

$$= 3.8 \text{ p.u.}$$

Example 47

A symmetrical short circuit is suddenly applied to a synchronous generator on open circuit, terminal voltage 1.0 p.u. The initial peak values of the symmetrical oscillogram of s.c. current are 8.0 p.u., 5.7 p.u., and 1.8 p.u.

(a) Neglecting resistance, it is required to determine the synchronous, transient and subtransient reactances.

(b) If the machine is delivering 1.0 p.u. current at 0.8 power factor lagging at the rated terminal voltage when the s.c. is applied, it is required to calculate the new current components for the oscillogram and to express the s.c. current in exponential form.

Solution.   (Ref. 2, p. 191)

(a) No load condition; $I_{\text{load}} = 0$, $E = E' = E'' = V = 1.0$ p.u.

With $R = 0$, the reactances are generally,

$$X = \frac{E}{I_{RMS}} = \frac{\sqrt{2}E}{I_{peak}}$$

Hence,

$$\text{synchronous } X_s = \frac{\sqrt{2} \times 1}{1.8} = 0.79 \text{ p.u.}$$

$$\text{transient } X' = \frac{\sqrt{2} \times 1}{5.7} = 0.25 \text{ p.u.}$$

$$\text{sub-transient } X'' = \frac{\sqrt{2} \times 1}{8.0} = 0.177 \text{ p.u.}$$

(b) On load condition;

Then
$$I_L = 1.0(0.8 - j0.6) \text{ p.u.}$$

$$E = V + jI_L X_s = 1.0 + j0.79(0.8 - j0.6)$$
$$= 1.474 + j0.63$$

$$E' = V + jI_L X' = 1.0 + j0.25(0.8 - j0.6)$$
$$= 1.15 + j0.20$$

$$E'' = V + jI_L X'' = 1.0 + j0.177(0.8 - j0.6)$$
$$= 1.106 + j0.14$$

RMS values of the currents;

$$|I_s| = \frac{|E|}{X_s} = \frac{1.605}{0.79} = 2.04$$

$$|I'| = \frac{|E'|}{X'} = \frac{1.17}{0.25} = 4.7$$

$$|I''| = \frac{|E''|}{X''} \quad \frac{1.11}{0.177} = 6.28$$

For the symmetrical oscillogram, (no d.c. component), the peak values of current components are required, viz;

$$\text{Peak } I_s = \sqrt{2} \times 2.04 = 2.89 \text{ p.u.}$$

$$\text{Peak } I' = \sqrt{2} \times 4.7 = 6.65 \text{ p.u.}$$

$$\text{Peak } I'' = \sqrt{2} \times 6.28 = 8.88 \text{ p.u.}$$

With current symbols indicating peak values, we have,

$$\text{p.u. } i_{ac} = (\hat{I}'' - \hat{I}')\,\epsilon^{-t/T_d''} + (\hat{I}' - \hat{I}_s)\,\epsilon^{-t/T_d'} + \hat{I}_s$$
$$= (8.88 - 6.65)\,\epsilon^{-t/T_d''} + (6.65 - 2.89)\,\epsilon^{-t/T_d'} + 2.89$$
$$= 2.24\,\epsilon^{-t/T_d''} + 3.76\,\epsilon^{-t/T_d'} + 2.89$$

Example 48

A 75 MVA 11 kV salient-pole synchronous generator is connected to infinite busbars through a reactor of value 0.3 p.u. The generator has $X_d = 1.5$ p.u., $X_q = 1.0$ p.u. and negligible resistance. It is required to:

(a) determine the power output for a load angle of 30° elect. and excitation 1.4 times the terminal voltage, and

(b) calculate the synchronising coefficient in this condition. All p.u. values refer to the machine rating.

Solution.   (Ref. 2, p. 178)

The power output of a salient-pole machine is given,

$$P = \frac{VE}{X_d}\sin\delta + \frac{V^2(X_d - X_q)}{2X_d X_q}\sin 2\delta \qquad \text{watt/phase}$$

With an external line impedance, $(X = 0.3 \text{ p.u.})$, the equation becomes;

$$P = \frac{VE}{(X_d + X)}\sin\delta + \frac{V^2[(X_d + X) - (X_q + X)]}{2(X_d + X)(X_q + X)}\sin 2\delta$$

Working in p.u. values,

$$P = \frac{1.0 \times 1.4}{(1.5 + 0.3)}\sin 30° + \frac{1[(1.5 + 0.3) - (1.0 + 0.3)]}{2(1.5 + 0.3)(1.0 + 0.3)}\sin 60°$$

$$= \frac{1.4}{1.8}(0.5) + \frac{1(0.5 \times 0.866)}{2(1.8 \times 1.3)}$$

$$= 0.48 \text{ p.u.}$$

(b) The synchronising coefficient is obtained,

$$\frac{\partial P}{\partial \delta} = \frac{VE}{(X_d + X)}\cos\delta + \frac{V^2[(X_d + X) - (X_q + X)]}{(X_d + X)(X_q + X)}\cos 2\delta$$

$$= \frac{1.4}{1.8}\cos 30° + \frac{0.5}{(1.8 \times 1.3)}\cos 60°$$

$$= 0.78 \text{ p.u.}$$

Example 49

A 3-phase synchronous generator of nominal rating 2000 kVA 11 kV supplies 1000 kW to a synchronous motor operating at 0.8 p.f. leading at a motor terminal voltage of 10.6 kV. Each machine has a subtransient reactance of 0.2 p.u. and the machines are connected by a line of reactance 0.1 p.u. It is required to calculate the subtransient current in the generator, in the motor and in the fault due to a symmetrical 3-phase fault at the motor terminals. Per unit values are based on the generator nominal rating.

Solution

The system may be represented as in Fig. 49.

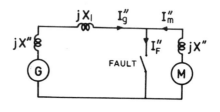

Fig. 49

Adopting the given base rating, and with motor terminal voltage, V_{tm} as reference phasor,

$$V_{tm} = 10.6 \, kV = \frac{10.6}{11.0} \underline{/0^\circ} = 0.964 \underline{/0^\circ} \text{ p.u.}$$

$$\text{Base current} = \frac{2000}{\sqrt{3} \times 11.0} = 105 \text{ A}$$

Before the fault, load current,

$$I_L = \frac{1000}{\sqrt{3} \times 10.6 \times 0.8} \underline{/36.9^\circ}$$

$$= 68.09 \underline{/36.9^\circ} \text{ amp} = 0.65 \underline{/36.9^\circ} \text{ p.u.}$$

$$= 0.65(0.8 + j0.6) = (0.52 + j0.39) \text{ p.u.}$$

For the generator;

$$V_{tg} = V_{tm} + jX_1 I_L = (0.964) + j0.1(0.52 + j0.39)$$

$$= (0.925 + j0.052) \text{ p.u.}$$

Voltage behind subtransient reactance,

$$E_g'' = V_{tg} + jX''I_L = (0.925 + j0.052) + j0.2(0.52 - j0.39)$$

$$= 0.847 + j0.156 \text{ p.u.}$$

$$\therefore \quad I_g'' = \frac{E_g''}{j(X'' + X_1)} = \frac{0.847 + j0.156}{j(0.2 + 0.1)} = 0.52 - j2.82 \text{ p.u.}$$

$$= 105(0.52 - j2.82) = (54.6 - j296.1) \text{ amp}$$

$$= 301.09 \underline{/-79.55°} \text{ amp}$$

For the motor;

$$V_{tm} = 0.964 \underline{/0°} \quad \text{(as above)}$$

$$E_m'' = V_{tm} - jX''I_L = 0.964 + j0 - j0.2(0.52 + j0.39)$$

$$= 1.042 - j0.104 \text{ p.u.}$$

$$I_m'' = \frac{E_m''}{jX''} = \frac{1.042 - j0.104}{j0.2} = (-0.52 - j5.21) \text{ p.u.}$$

$$= 105(-0.52 - j5.21) = (-54.6 - j547.05) \text{ amp}$$

$$= -549.77 \underline{/84.30°} \text{ amp}$$

Current in Fault,

$$I_F'' = I_g'' + I_m''$$

$$= (54.6 - j296.1) + (-54.6 - j547.05)$$

$$= -j843.15 \text{ amp}$$

Alternative solution by Thévenin theorem applied to network; Impedance behind faulted terminals,

$$Z_{Th} = \frac{j0.3 \times j0.2}{j0.3 + j0.2} = j0.12 \text{ p.u.}$$

$$V_{tm} = 0.964 \underline{/0°} \text{ p.u.}$$

$$\therefore \quad I_F'' = \frac{0.964 + j0}{j0.12} = -j8.03 \text{ p.u.}$$

$$= 105(-j8.03) = -j843.15 \text{ amp}$$

The components of current to the fault from the machines are divided inversely as the impedances, viz.,

$$I_{gF}'' = \left(\frac{X_m''}{X_g'' + X_m''}\right)I_F'' = \frac{0.2}{0.5}\left(-j8.03\right)$$

$$= -j3.212 \text{ p.u.}$$

$$I''_{mF} = \left(\frac{X''_g}{X''_g + X''_m}\right) I''_F = \frac{0.3}{0.5}(-8.03)$$

$$= -j4.818 \text{ p.u.}$$

Now, prefault current, $I_L = (0.52 + j0.39)$ p.u. Therefore total subtransient currents in the machines,

$$I''_g = I''_{gF} + I_L = (0.52 - j2.82) \text{ p.u.}$$

$$I''_m = I''_{mF} - I_L = (-0.52 - j5.21) \text{ p.u.}$$

as before.

Example 50

A synchronous motor, with stator resistance R ohms/phase, operates with constant mechanical output on constant voltage V/phase busbars. Show that the current phasor, $\overline{OB}$, generally at phase angle ϕ to the V-phasor, lies on a circular locus:

(a) of diameter $\overline{OA} = V/R$ along the V-phasor, for the limiting case of constant zero gross power output,

(b) under conditions of constant power output, P_0, of radius

$$\left\{\left(\frac{V}{2R}\right)^2 - \frac{P_0}{R}\right\}^{1/2}$$

and concentric with the circle on $\overline{OA}$.

Solution.   (Ref. 4, p. 399)

Part (a).   Power input/phase $= VI \cos \phi$

Gross power output/phase, $P_0 = VI \cos \phi - I^2 R$

(N.B.   Gross P_0 = nett shaft output + friction, windage + core losses).
For the limiting case, $P_0 = VI \cos \phi - I^2 R = 0$

Thus $VI \cos \phi = I^2 R$

$$I = \frac{V}{R} \cos \phi = \text{a circular locus for constant } \frac{V}{R}$$

Referring to the Fig. 50 we have,

$$V(\overline{OC}) = (\overline{OB})^2 R$$

Since B lies on a circle, then $(\overline{OB})^2 R = (\overline{OC})(\overline{OA}) R$

$$\therefore \qquad \overline{OA} = \frac{V}{R} = \text{constant diameter,} \quad \text{as required}$$

Part (b).   Referring to Fig. 50.

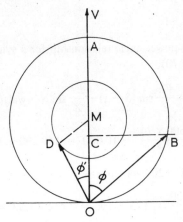

Fig. 50

Consider a current $I = \overline{OD}$, corresponding to a constant P_0, where $P_0 = VI \cos \phi' - I^2 R$

$$(\overline{MD})^2 = (\overline{OD})^2 + (\overline{OM})^2 - 2(\overline{OD})(\overline{OM}) \cos \phi'$$

$$= I^2 + \left(\frac{V}{2R}\right)^2 - 2(I)\left(\frac{V}{2R}\right) \cos \phi'$$

$$= \left(\frac{V}{2R}\right)^2 - \frac{1}{R}(VI \cos \phi' - I^2 R)$$

$$= \left(\frac{V}{2R}\right)^2 - \frac{P_0}{R}$$

Hence

$$MD = \left\{ \left(\frac{V}{2R}\right)^2 - \frac{P_0}{R} \right\}^{1/2} = \text{constant for constant } V, R \text{ and } P_0$$

(N.B.   Compare this proof with Example 51b recalling that Z is a constant operator.)

Example 51

A 3-phase 600-hp, 3000 V, Y-connected synchronous motor has a synchronous impedance/phase of $(2 + j10)$ ohm. Determine the full-load current and power factor when the excitation is 1.33 p.u. The iron, friction, windage and excitation losses are 10 kW/phase. What value of excitation would give unity power factor on full load? A graphical method of solution may be used.

Solution

(a) *Analytical.* The power/angle relationship for a synchronous motor may be stated (Ref. 2, p. 170),

$$P_0 = \frac{VE}{Z} \sin (\delta + \alpha) - \frac{E^2}{Z} \sin \alpha \quad \text{watt/phase}$$

Given

$$P_0 = \frac{600 \times 746}{3} + 10\,000 = 149\,200 + 10\,000$$

$$= 159\,200 \text{ watt/phase}$$

Now

$$V = \frac{3000}{\sqrt{3}} = 1732; \quad E = 1732 \times 1.33 = 2304.$$

$$Z = (2^2 + 10^2)^{1/2} = 10.2 \text{ ohm}; \quad \sin \alpha = \frac{2}{10.2} = 0.1963$$

Then $\alpha = 11°19'$.

Substituting in equation for P_0 we have,

$$\frac{1732 \times 2304}{10.2} \sin (\delta + \alpha) = 159\,200 + \frac{(2304)^2 \times 0.196}{10.2}$$

$$391 \times 10^3 \sin (\delta + \alpha) = 159\,200 + 10.2 \times 10^4$$

$$= 261\,200$$

$$\sin (\delta + \alpha) = \frac{261\,200}{391\,000} = 0.668$$

$$(\delta + \alpha) = 41°55'$$

$$\delta = (41°55' - 11°19') = 30°36'$$

From the voltage phasor diagram, (Fig. 51(a))

$$(IZ)^2 = V^2 + E^2 - 2VE \cos \delta$$

$$= (1732)^2 + (2304)^2 - (2 \times 1732 \times 2304 \times 0.86)$$

$$= 3 \times 10^6 + 5.3 \times 10^6 - 6.86 \times 10^6 = 1.44 \times 10^6$$

$$IZ = 1.2 \times 10^3 \text{ volt}$$

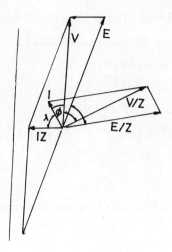

Fig. 51(a)

$\therefore$ $$I = \frac{1200}{10.2} = 117 \text{ amp}$$

Now

input power, $P_i = VI \cos \phi = P_0 + I^2 R$

$$= 159.2 \times 10^3 + 27.4 \times 10^3 = 186.6 \times 10^3 \text{ watt/phase}$$

$\therefore$ $$\cos \phi = \frac{186.6 \times 10^3}{1732 \times 117} = 0.92 \quad \text{leading}$$

Second part:

$$P_0 = 159.2 \times 10^3 \text{ watt/phase} \quad \text{(unchanged)}$$

$$P_i = P_0 + I^2 R = 159.2 \times 10^3 + 2I^2$$

$$= VI \cos \phi = 1732I \quad \text{at unity power factor}$$

Then

$$2I^2 - 1732I + 159.2 \times 10^3 = 0$$

$\therefore$ $$I = \frac{+1732 \pm \sqrt{\{(1732)^2 - (4)(2)(159.2 \times 10^3)\}}}{4}$$

$$= \frac{1732 \pm \sqrt{(1726 \times 10^6)}}{4}$$

$$= \frac{1732 \pm 1314}{4} = \frac{3038}{4} \quad \text{or} \quad \frac{418}{4}$$

Now $= 104.5$ amp   (using the preferred value)

$$IR = 104.5 \times 2 = 209 \text{ volt}; \quad IX = 104.5 \times 10 = 1045 \text{ volt}$$

From the unity-power-factor phasor diagram;

$$E^2 = (V - IR)^2 + (IX)^2$$
$$= (1732 - 209)^2 + (1045)^2$$
$$= (1523)^2 + (1045)^2 = 2.32 \times 10^6 + 1.09 \times 10^6$$
$$= 3.41 \times 10^6$$
$$E = 1847 \text{ volt} = 1.07 \text{ p.u.}$$

(b) *Graphical solution*:   The method employs the current locus proved in Example 50 and extended as follows (Fig. 51(b)):

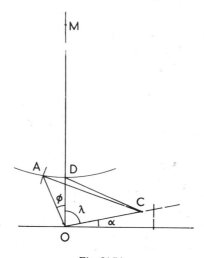

Fig. 51(b)

Phasors IZ, V and E form the sides of a voltage triangle. Since Z is constant, the phasors I, V/Z and E/Z will form a similar triangle. Note that Z is an operator $= Z \underline{/\lambda}$ where $\lambda = \tan^{-1} X/R$. Hence the current phasors each lie $\underline{/\lambda}$ behind the corresponding voltage phasor.

For the given problem we have;

$$V = \frac{3000}{\sqrt{3}} = 1732 \text{ volt}; \quad E = 1732 \times 1.33 = 2304 \text{ volt}$$

$$Z = 10.2 \text{ ohm}$$

Then

$$\frac{V}{Z} = \frac{1732}{10.2} = 170, \quad \frac{E}{Z} = \frac{2304}{10.2} = 225.9$$

$$P_0 = \frac{600 \times 746}{3} + 10\,000 = 159\,200 \text{ watt/phase}$$

Referring to Fig. 51(b).

Choose a current scale, say 1 cm = 20 amp. Draw

$$\overline{OM} = \frac{V}{2R} = \frac{1732}{4} = 433 \text{ amp} = 21.65 \text{ cm}$$

Radius of O-curve for the given P_0

$$= \left\{ \left(\frac{V}{2R} \right)^2 - \frac{P_0}{R} \right\}^{1/2} = \left\{ (433)^2 - \frac{159\,200}{2} \right\}^{1/2}$$

$$= \sqrt{(187\,500 - 79\,600)} = 328.5$$

With centre M, draw arc of radius $\overline{MD} = 328.5$ amp $= 16.4$ cm. Draw

$$\overline{CO} = \frac{V}{Z} = 170 \text{ amp} = 8.5 \text{ cm}$$

at an angle λ to $\overline{OM}$, (where $\lambda = \tan^{-1} X/R = \tan^{-1} 10/2$).

Describe an arc of radius

$$\overline{CA} = \frac{E}{Z} = 225.9 \text{ amp} = 11.3 \text{ cm}$$

$$\text{Measure } \overline{OA} = 5.8 \text{ cm} = 116 \text{ amp} = I$$

$$\underline{/\phi} = 22.5° \quad \text{and} \quad \cos\phi = 0.92 \text{ leading}$$

Last part: At unity power factor,

$$\text{Measure } \overline{CD} = 9.05 = \frac{E}{Z}$$

∴ $\qquad E = 9.05 \times 10.2 \times 20 = 1844 \text{ volt} = 1.07 \text{ p.u.}$

Example 52

A 3 phase star-connected 30 hp synchronous motor is connected to a 500 V supply and has synchronous impedance of $(0.4 + j4)$ ohm/phase. The mechanical, excitation and iron losses are assumed constant at 1500 W. Calculate the maximum load as a percentage of full load when the excitation gives an induced voltage of 300 V/phase. Determine the current and power factor under these maximum conditions.

Solution

The power/angle relationship for a synchronous motor may be stated (Ref. 2, p. 170),

$$P_0 = \frac{VE}{Z} \sin(\delta + \alpha) - \frac{E^2}{Z} \sin \alpha \quad \text{watt/phase}$$

$$\text{Maximum } P_0 = \frac{VE}{Z} - \frac{E^2}{Z} \sin \alpha$$

Now

$$|Z| = (0.4^2 + 4^2)^{1/2} = 4.02 \text{ ohm}; \quad \sin \alpha = \frac{R}{Z} = \frac{0.4}{4.02} = 0.0995$$

and $\alpha = 5°43'$. Also $V = 500/\sqrt{3} = 289$ volt.

$$\therefore \qquad \text{Max } P_0 = \frac{289 \times 300}{4.02} - \frac{(300)^2}{4.02} \times 0.0995$$

$$= 21\,570 - 2227 = 19\,343 \text{ watt/phase}$$

$$\text{Max useful } P_0 = 19\,343 - \frac{1500}{3} = 18\,843 \text{ watt/phase}$$

$$\text{Max power} = \frac{3 \times 18\,843}{746} = 75.77 \text{ hp (or 56.524 kW)}$$

$$= \frac{75.77 \times 100}{30} = 252.6\% \text{ F.L.}$$

Maximum power occurs when $(\delta + \alpha) = 90°$, that is, when $\delta = 90° - 5°43' = 84°17'$.

From the voltage phasor diagram, Fig. 52

$$(IZ)^2 = V^2 + E^2 - 2VE \cos \delta$$

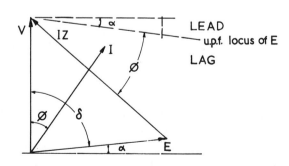

Fig. 52

$$= (289)^2 + (300)^2 - 2(289)(300)(0.099)$$

$$= 83\,520 + 90\,000 - 17\,260$$

$$= 156\,260$$

$$IZ = 395.3$$

$$I = \frac{395.3}{4.02} = 98.33 \text{ amp}$$

Now

$$\text{copper loss} = I^2 R = (98.33)^2 \times 0.4 = 3867 \text{ watt}$$

∴   Input/phase $= 19\,343 + 3867 = 23\,210$ watt

$$= VI \cos \phi$$

∴ $\cos \phi = \dfrac{23\,210}{289 \times 98.33} = 0.8167$ lagging

Example 53

A 3-phase 50 Hz Y-connected synchronous motor takes 600 A at unity power factor from 11 kV busbars. The machine has a stator impedance of $(0.5 + j8)$ ohm/phase. Calculate
   (a) the load angle,
   (b) the percentage change in excitation necessary to enable the machine to operate at a leading power factor of 0.6, with unchanged electrical power input.

Solution

The power/angle relationship for the electrical power input to a synchronous motor can be stated (Ref. 2, p. 170)

$$P_i = \frac{VE}{Z_s} \sin(\delta - \alpha) + \frac{V^2}{Z_s} \sin \alpha \quad \text{watt/phase}$$

The simplest solution is obtained from consideration of the phasor diagram, Fig. 53. This may be treated analytically, or graphically by drawing the diagram to scale. The above equation shows that the limit of stability occurs when $(\delta - \alpha) = 90°$. Analytical;

$$V = \frac{11 \times 10^3}{\sqrt{3}} = 6351 \text{ volt/phase}$$

The geometry of the phasor diagram gives,

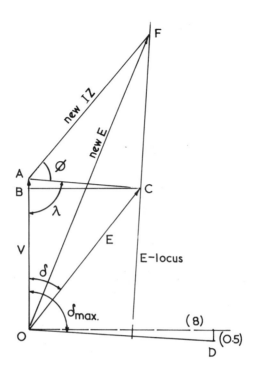

Fig. 53

$$E^2 = (V - IR)^2 + (IX)^2 = (6351 - 300)^2 + (4800)^2$$
$$= 36.63 \times 10^6 + 23.03 \times 10^6 = 59.7 \times 10^6$$
$$E = 7723 \text{ volt}$$

$$\sin \delta = \frac{IX}{E} = \frac{4800}{7723} = 0.6215$$

$\therefore$ 　　　　　$\delta = 38.4°$ 　or 　$38°26'$

Now

power input/phase $= VI \cos \phi = 6351 \times 600 \times 1.0$
$$= 3810.6 \times 10^3 \text{ watt} = \text{constant}$$

$$\text{New } I = \frac{3810.6 \times 10^3}{6351 \times 0.6} = 1000 \text{ amp}$$

$$|Z| = (R^2 + X^2)^{1/2} = 8.015 \text{ ohm}$$

$$\text{New } IZ = 8015 \text{ volt}$$

Now
$$E^2 = (IZ)^2 + V^2 - 2V(IZ)\cos(\lambda + \phi)$$

$$\left.\begin{array}{l} \lambda = \tan^{-1} X/R = 86.4° \\ \phi = \cos^{-1} 0.6 = 53.1° \end{array}\right\}(\lambda + \phi) = 139.5°$$

$$\cos(\lambda + \phi) = -\cos 40.5° = -0.7608$$

Hence

$$\text{New } E^2 = (8015)^2 + (6351)^2 + 2(6351)(8015)(0.7608)$$

$$= 64.12 \times 10^6 + 40.33 \times 10^6 + 77.29 \times 10^6$$

$$= 181.74 \times 10^6$$

∴ New $E = 13.48 \times 10^3 = 13\,480$ volt

This gives $(13\,480 - 7723) = 5757$ volts $= 74.5\%$ increase.

Graphical procedure: Choose a voltage scale, say 1 cm = 2000 volt.

Draw $V = 6351$ volt $= 3.18$ cm $=$ OA vertically.

Draw $IR = 300$ volt $= 0.15$ cm $=$ AB

Draw $IX = 4800$ volt $= 2.4$ cm $=$ BC, perpendicular to AB.

Draw OD at angle $\alpha = \tan^{-1} 0.5/8$, to horizontal at O, (8 arbitrary units horizontal, 0.5 arbitrary units vertical).

This defines the stability limit.

Erect a perpendicular to OD to pass through C. This is the E-locus for constant electrical power.

At A draw the new $IZ = $ AF, at $\phi (= \cos^{-1} 0.6 = 53.15°)$ to AC, meeting the E-locus at F.

$$OF = 6.75 \text{ cm} = 13\,500 \text{ volt} = \text{new } E$$

Thus

$$OF - OC = (13\,500 - 7723) = 5777 \text{ volt}$$

$$= 74.8\% \quad \text{increase}$$

Chapter Five

Induction Motors

Example 54

A 3 phase 4 pole 50 Hz induction motor has a rotor impedance of $(0.06 + j0.5)$ ohm/phase at standstill. The maximum torque which it can develop is 200 newton metre. Find

(a) the speed at maximum torque,
(b) the torque at starting,
(c) the running speed when the torque is 100 newton metre.

Solution

The torque developed by an m-phase induction motor having p pairs of poles is expressed, (Ref. 2, p. 219; Ref. 4, p. 254)

$$\text{ⓉT} = \frac{m}{\omega_s k^2}\left[\frac{sV^2R_r}{R_r^2 + (s\omega L_r)^2}\right]\text{newton metre}$$

where $\omega_s = 2\pi f/p$ mech rad/sec and $\omega = 2\pi f$ elect rad/sec and

$$k = \frac{\text{stator turns/phase}}{\text{rotor turns/phase}}$$

With constant supply volts, V/phase, and const. frequency, f, torque may be stated,

$$\text{ⓉT} = K\frac{sR_r}{R_r^2 + (s\omega L_r)^2} \quad \text{where} \quad K = \text{constant}$$

Part (a). The condition for max torque occurs when $d\text{ⓉT}/ds = 0$ and is $R_r = (s\omega L_r)$. Then

$$s = R_r/(\omega L_r) = 0.06/0.5 = 0.12 \qquad \frac{50}{2} = 25 = n$$

and

$$\text{speed} = N_{\text{syn}}(1 - s) = 1500 \times 0.88 = 1320 \text{ rpm.}$$

Part (b). At starting, $s = 1.0$

$$\therefore \qquad \text{ⓉT}_{\text{start}} = K\frac{R_r}{R_r^2 + (\omega L_r)^2}$$

But when $R_r = (s\omega L_r)$, $\text{ⓉT}_{\text{max}} = K/2(\omega L_r)$. Then

$$\frac{\text{ⓉT}_{\text{start}}}{\text{ⓉT}_{\text{max}}} = \frac{2(\omega L_r)(R_r)}{R_r^2 + (\omega L_r)^2} = \frac{2 \times 0.06 \times 0.5}{(0.06)^2 + (0.5)^2}$$

$$= \frac{0.06}{0.2536}$$

$$\therefore \qquad \textcircled{T}_{start} = \frac{0.06 \times 200}{0.2536} = 47.3 \text{ newton metre}$$

Part (c)

$$\frac{\textcircled{T}}{\textcircled{T}_{max}} = \frac{(sR_r)(2\omega L_r)}{R_r^2 + (s\omega L_r)^2}$$

$$\frac{100}{200} = \frac{(0.06s)(2 \times 0.5)}{(0.06)^2 + (0.5s)^2}$$

$$0.25 s^2 - 0.12 s + 36 \times 10^{-4} = 0$$

$$s = \frac{+0.12 \pm \sqrt{\{144 \times 10^{-4} - 4(0.25)(36 \times 10^{-4})\}}}{0.5}$$

$$= \frac{+0.12 \pm \sqrt{(108 \times 10^{-4})}}{0.5}$$

$$= (0.4476) \quad \text{or} \quad 0.0322$$

Then

$$\text{speed} = N_{syn}(1 - s)$$

$$= 1500(0.9678) = 1452 \text{ rpm}$$

The alternative value for s gives speed = 830 rpm in the unstable region of operation.

Example 55

The approximate equivalent circuit/phase of a 3-phase, 4-pole 50 Hz, 420 V induction motor with a mesh-connected stator winding is given in Fig. 55. V = phase voltage, s = slip and the numerical values are in ohms. Calculate the input current, power factor, output power and the efficiency for the machine on load when running at 1455 rpm.

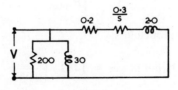

Fig. 55

Solution.   (Ref. 4, p. 263)

At 1455 rpm,

$$\text{slip} = \frac{1500 - 1455}{1500} = 0.03$$

Impedance of the series elements

$$= 0.2 + \frac{0.3}{0.03} + j2$$

$$= 10.2 + j2$$

Admittance of series elements,

$$Y_s = \frac{10.2 - j2}{108.04}$$

$$= 0.094 - j0.018$$

$$\text{Magnitude,} \; |Y_s| = 0.0957 = 0.096$$

$$\text{Admittance of shunt branch} = \frac{1}{200} - \frac{j}{30} = 0.005 - j0.033$$

$$\text{Total admittance,} \; Y = 0.099 - j0.051 = 0.11 \underline{/-27.2^\circ}$$

$$\text{Input current/phase} = VY = (420 \times 0.11) \underline{/-27.2^\circ} = 46.2 \underline{/-27.2^\circ}$$

∴ $$\text{Input current, (line value)} = \sqrt{3} \times 46.2 \underline{/-27.2^\circ}$$

$$= 80.0 \underline{/-27.2^\circ} \; \text{amp}$$

$$\text{Power factor} = \cos 27.2^\circ = 0.89 \; \text{lagging}$$

$$\text{Input power} = 3V_{ph}I_{ph} \cos \phi = (3 \times 420 \times 46.2 \times 0.89) \; \text{watt}$$

$$= 51.8 \; \text{kW}$$

Now,

$$\text{current in series elements} = 420 \times 0.096 = 40.32 \; \text{A/ph}$$

∴ $$\text{Total rotor cu loss} = 3(40.32)^2 \times 0.3 = 1463 \; \text{watt}$$

Output can be represented/phase by a resistor

$$= \left(\frac{1 - s}{s}\right) R_{\text{rotor}}$$

Therefore in terms of rotor cu loss,

$$\text{Output power} = 1463 \times \left(\frac{0.97}{0.03}\right)$$

$$= 47.3 \; \text{kW}$$

$$\text{Efficiency} = \frac{\text{output power}}{\text{input power}} = \frac{47.3}{51.8} = 0.913$$

$$= 91.3\%$$

Example 56

A 415 V, 50 Hz 3 phase Y-connected 4 pole induction motor has full load slip of 4%. The standstill rotor impedance/phase is $(0.1 + j0.9)$ ohm and the ratio stator/rotor turns/phase is 2. Calculate:

(a) the full load torque,

(b) the rotor starter-resistance/phase to give 150% full load torque at starting, with minimum current.

Solution.   (Ref. 2, p. 219; Ref. 4, p. 254)

Part (a). $V = 415/\sqrt{3} = 240$ volt; $\omega_s = 2\pi f/p = 50\pi$

$$\widehat{T} = \frac{m}{\omega_s k^2}\left[\frac{sV^2R_r}{R_r^2 + (s\omega L_r)^2}\right] \text{newton metre}$$

$$= \frac{3}{50\pi(2)^2}\left[\frac{0.04 \times (240)^2 \times 0.1}{(0.1)^2 + (0.04 \times 0.9)^2}\right]$$

$$= \frac{691.2}{50\pi \times 4 \times (0.01 + 0.0013)}$$

$$= 97.3 \text{ newton metre}$$

Part (b).   With constant V and f,

$$\widehat{T} = K\frac{sR_r}{R_r^2 + (s\omega L_r)^2} \quad \text{where} \quad K = \text{constant}$$

At full load, $s = 0.04$

$\therefore$

$$\widehat{T}_{FL} = K\frac{0.04 \times 0.1}{(0.1)^2 + (0.04 \times 0.9)^2}$$

$$= K\left(\frac{0.004}{0.0113}\right)$$

$$1.5\,\widehat{T}_{FL} = K\left(\frac{0.006}{0.0113}\right)$$

At start, $s = 1.0$

$$\therefore \quad \textcircled{T}_{start} = K \frac{R_r}{R_r^2 + (\omega L_r)^2}$$

$$= K \frac{R_r}{R_r^2 + 0.81} = 1.5 \, \textcircled{T}_{FL}$$

$$0.006 R_r^2 - 0.0113 R_r + 0.004\,86 = 0$$

$$6 R_r^2 - 11.3 R_r + 4.86 = 0$$

$$R_r = \frac{+11.3 \pm \sqrt{\{(11.3)^2 - (4)(6)(4.86)\}}}{12}$$

$$= \frac{11.3 \pm \sqrt{(127.7 - 116.7)}}{12} = \frac{11.3 \pm 3.332}{12}$$

$$= \frac{14.632}{12} = 1.219 \text{ ohm} \quad \text{(preferred value)}$$

$$\therefore \qquad \text{Added } R_r = (1.219 - 0.1) = 1.119 \text{ ohm/phase.}$$

N.B.   The preferred solution here gives higher starting resistance and hence the lower starting current.

Example 57

A 415 V, 50 Hz 3 phase Y-connected 4-pole induction motor develops maximum torque of 152 newton metre at starting. The added rotor resistance/phase at start is 0.8 ohm. The ratio of stator to rotor turns/phase is 2. Calculate:

(a) rotor winding impedance at standstill,

(b) the running speed and the rotor current when the output power developed is 20 hp. (**N.B.**   1 hp = 746 W).

Solution

$$V = 415/\sqrt{3} = 240 \text{ volt}; \omega_s = 2\pi f/p = 50\pi.$$

Part (a).   The condition for max torque occurs when $dT/ds = 0$ and is $R_r = (s\omega L_r)$. At this condition, (Ref. 2, p. 220)

$$\textcircled{T}_{max} = \frac{mV^2}{2k^2 \omega_s (\omega L_r)} = 152 \text{ newton metre}$$

$$\therefore \qquad \omega L_r = \frac{mV^2}{2k^2 \omega_s T_{max}} = \frac{3 \times (240)^2}{2 \times 4 \times 50\pi \times 152}$$

$$= \frac{172\,800}{191\,000} = 0.9 \text{ ohm}$$

$$= \text{rotor resistance at start}$$

$$= (R_r + 0.8)$$

$$\therefore \qquad R_r = 0.1 \text{ ohm}$$

Hence standstill rotor impedance $= (0.1 + j0.9)$ ohm/phase.

Part (b)(i)

$$\omega_r = \omega_s(1 - s)$$

$$\omega_r \, \textcircled{T} = \frac{m(1 - s)}{k^2}\left[\frac{sV^2R_r}{R_r^2 + (s\omega L_r)^2}\right]$$

$$20 \times 746 = \frac{3(1 - s)}{4}\left[\frac{s(240)^2(0.1)}{(0.1)^2 + (0.9s)^2}\right]$$

$$14\,920 = \frac{17\,280(s - s^2)}{0.04 + 3.24s^2}$$

$$596.8 + 48\,340s^2 = 17\,280s - 17\,280s^2$$

$$65\,620s^2 - 17\,280s + 596.8 = 0$$

$$\therefore \qquad s = \frac{+17\,280 \pm \sqrt{297.9 \times 10^6 - 156.6 \times 10^6})}{131\,240}$$

$$= \frac{17.28 \times 10^3 \pm 11.88 \times 10^3}{131.24 \times 10^3}$$

$$= 0.0411 \quad \text{(using preferred value)}$$

$$N_r = N_{syn}(1 - s) = 1500 \times 0.9589 = 1438 \text{ rpm}$$

Part (b)(ii) Rotor current/phase,

$$I_r = \frac{sV}{k\{R_r^2 + (s\omega L_r)^2\}^{1/2}}$$

$$= \frac{0.0412 \times 240}{2\{(0.1)^2 + (0.0412 \times 0.9)^2\}^{1/2}}$$

$$= \frac{9.888}{2(0.01 + 0.001\,37)^{1/2}} = \frac{9.888}{0.214}$$

$$= 46.2 \text{ amp/phase.}$$

Check

Rotor copper loss $= I_r^2R_r = (46.2)^2(0.1) = 213.4 \text{ W/ph.}$

$$= 637.5 \text{ watt} \quad \text{for 3 phases}$$

$$\text{Rotor output} = 14\,920 \text{ watt}$$

$$\text{Rotor input} = 14\,920 + 637.5 = 15\,557.5 \text{ watt}$$

$$\text{Slip} = \frac{\text{Rotor cu loss}}{\text{Rotor input}} = \frac{637.5}{15\,557.5} = 0.0412$$

Example 58

The following specification applies to a 3-phase induction motor: 20 hp, 440 V, 50 Hz, 4-pole, star-connected stator.
No-load test results; 440 V, 10 A, p.f. 0.2 lagging.
Standstill test results; 200 V, 50 A, p.f. 0.4 lagging.
  Draw the Circle Diagram and from it determine;
  (a) full-load current and power factor,
  (b) the maximum output power,
  (c) the stalling torque.
Assume the rotor and stator copper losses on short-circuit to be equal.

Solution.   (Ref. 2, p. 221; Ref. 4, 274)

The Circle Diagram is a popular and convenient method of obtaining an approximate prediction of machine performance. It is based upon the phasor diagram which is derived from the equivalent circuit. It is consequently subject to the same limitations of accuracy (Refs. 2, 4 and 6).
  Working PER PHASE and with the test figures given;
  (i) Choose a Current Scale, say 1 cm = 10 A. Then

$$\text{Power Scale is 1 cm} = (\text{current scale} \times \text{phase volts})$$

$$= 10 \times \frac{440}{\sqrt{3}} = 2540 \text{ watt/phase}$$

$$\text{Torque Scale is 1 cm} = \frac{\text{power scale}}{\text{synchronous speed in mech rads/sec}}$$

$$= \frac{2540}{(2\pi f/p)} = \frac{2540}{(314/2)} = 16.18 \text{ Nm/phase}$$

(ii) Reference Fig. 58, draw OV vertical to represent the V-phasor direction. Scale 10 arbitrary units along OV and draw the P.F. Quadrant Circle.
  (iii) Draw $I_0 = 10 \text{ A} = 1 \text{ cm}$ in magnitude, and at 0.2 p.f. relative to OV. Adjust I_s to the rated voltage by direct proportion, viz.,

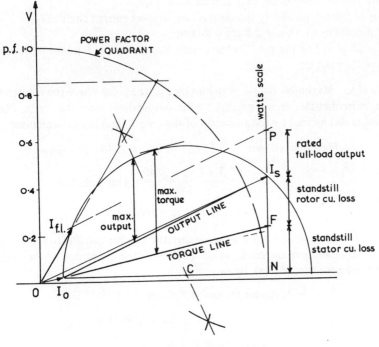

Fig. 58

$$I_s = 50 \times \frac{440}{200} = 110 \, \text{A} \quad \text{at 0.4 p.f. (unchanged)}$$

Draw $I_s = 110 \, \text{A} = 11 \, \text{cm}$ in magnitude, at 0.4 p.f. to OV.
Join $I_0 I_s$. This is the OUTPUT LINE.
Draw the $\perp$ bisector of $I_0 I_s$ and thus determine point C.
This is the centre of the circle which forms the current-locus.

Divide $I_s N$ at F, where $I_s F / FN = \dfrac{\text{rotor cu loss}}{\text{stator cu loss}}$

Join FI_0. This is the TORQUE LINE.

Part (a). NI_s extended provides a convenient vertical for an output-watt scale. Now, given

$$\text{full-load output} = 20 \, \text{hp} = \frac{20 \times 746}{3} \, \text{watt/phase}$$

this measures,

$$\left(\frac{20 \times 746}{3}\right) \times \frac{1}{2540} = 1.96 \, \text{cm}$$

Mark this distance on the output watt scale $= I_s P$.

Project from P, parallel to the output line, to meet current circle at I_{f1}.

By measurement, $OI_{f1} = 2.8$ cm $= 28$ amp

OI_{f1} projected to the p.f. quadrant circle determines the full-load power factor $= 0.85$ lagging.

Part (b).   Maximum output is determined at the point where the tangent to the current-circle, drawn parallel to the output line, meet the circle. (The point is also located by the $\perp$ bisector of the output line). By measurement,

$$\text{Maximum output} = 3.55 \text{ cm} = 3.55 \times 2540 \text{ watts/phase}$$

$$= \frac{3 \times 3.55 \times 2540}{746} \quad \text{(for 3 phases)}$$

$$= 36.3 \text{ hp. or } 27.05 \text{ kW}$$

Part (c).   Maximum torque occurs where the tangent, parallel to the torque line, meets the current circle, (also located by the $\perp$ bisector of the chord containing the torque line). By measurement,

$$\text{Maximum torque} = 4.45 \text{ cm} = 4.45 \times 16.18$$

$$= 72.0 \text{ Nm/phase}$$

$$\therefore \quad \text{Stalling Torque} = 3 \times 72.0$$

$$= 216 \text{ Nm for 3-phases}$$

Example 59

A 3-phase, 16 hp, 400 V, 50 Hz, induction motor with a 6-pole, star-connected stator, gave the following test results;

No-load test; 400 volt, 11 amp, 1800 watt (line values).

Standstill test; 100 volt, 24 amp, 2060 watt (line values).

Stator winding resistance/phase $= 0.65$ ohm and stator/rotor transformation ratio $= 2$.

Calculate:

(a) the rotor starting-resistance to limit the starting current to 150% full-load current,

(b) the ratio of an auto-transformer to similarly limit the line current.

Determine the starting torque in each case.

Solution

From given test data,

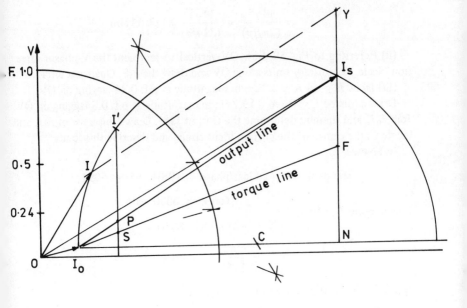

Fig. 59

$$\text{No-load p.f.} = \cos \phi_0 = \frac{1800}{\sqrt{3} \times 400 \times 11}$$

$$= 0.24 \text{ lag}$$

$$\text{Standstill test, p.f.} = \cos \phi_s = \frac{2060}{\sqrt{3} \times 100 \times 24} = 0.5 \text{ lag}$$

For a Circle Diagram solution: working per PHASE.
At rated voltage, by direct proportion,

$$I_s = 24 \times \frac{400}{100} = 96 \text{ A}$$

(i) Choose a current scale, say, 1 cm = 5 amp.
Then power scale is,

$$1 \text{ cm} = (\text{current scale} \times \text{phase volts})$$

$$= 5 \times \frac{400}{\sqrt{3}} = 1155 \text{ watts}$$

torque scale is,

$$1 \text{ cm} = \frac{\text{power scale}}{\text{syn speed in mech rad/sec}}$$

$$= \frac{1155}{(2\pi f/p)} = \frac{1155}{(314/3)} = 11.03\,\text{Nm}$$

(ii) Referring to Fig. 59 draw OV vertical to represent the V-phasor direction. Scale 10 arbitrary units along OV and draw the P.F. Quadrant circle.

(iii) Draw $I_0 = 11\,\text{A} = 2.2\,\text{cm}$ in magnitude at p.f. 0.24 lagging on OV.

Draw adjusted $I_s = 96\,\text{A} = 19.2\,\text{cm}$ in magnitude at p.f. 0.5 lagging on OV. Join $I_0 I_s$ and thereby determine the Output Line. Draw $\perp$ bisector of $I_0 I_s$ and locate C, the centre of the current-locus circle, and describe this locus.

(iv) Now,

$$\text{standstill stator cu loss/phase} = (96)^2 0.65 = 5991$$

$$\text{(say), } = 6000\,\text{watt}$$

Locate point F, where

$$FN = \text{stator cu loss/phase}$$

$$= \frac{6000}{1155} = 5.2\,\text{cm}$$

Join FI_0. This is the Torque Line.

Part (a).

$$\text{Full-load output} = 16\,\text{hp total} = \frac{16 \times 746}{3} = 3980\,\text{watt/phase}$$

and represented by

$$\frac{3980}{1155} = 3.45\,\text{cm}$$

Mark off $I_s Y = 3.45\,\text{cm}$ vertically.

Draw YI parallel to the Output Line to meet current circle at point I. Hence full-load current $= OI = 5.4\,\text{cm} = 27.0\,\text{amp}$.

$$\text{Mark off } 150\%\,I_{FL} = 1.5 \times 27.0 = 40.5\,\text{amp}$$

$$= 8.1\,\text{cm to scale} = OI'$$

$$\text{The corresponding torque} = I'S = 5.55\,\text{cm} = 5.55 \times 11.03\,\text{Nm}$$

$$= 61.2\,\text{Nm/phase} = 3 \times 61.2 \quad \text{(total)}$$

$$= 183.6\,\text{Nm} = \text{Starting Torque}$$

Standstill Rotor Cu loss

$$= I'P = 5\,\text{cm} = 5 \times 1155\,\text{watt/phase}$$

$$= 5775\,\text{watt/phase}$$

= watts dissipated in the rotor starting resistance.

∴   Added rotor resistance (referred to stator),

$$= \frac{5775}{(40.5)^2} = 3.52 \text{ ohm}$$

In rotor circuit,

$$\text{Added Rotor Resistance} = \frac{3.52}{(\text{transfr. ratio})^2}$$

$$= \frac{3.52}{4} = 0.88 \text{ ohm/phase.}$$

Part (b).   With auto-transformer start.

To limit line (motor) current to 150% I_{FL} we have,

$$\frac{\text{standstill amps}}{150\% \, I_{FL}} = \frac{96}{40.5} = 2.37$$

But volt step-down in transformer is current step-up. Hence

$$\text{ratio required} = \left(\frac{40.5}{96}\right)^{1/2} = 0.65$$

that is, Auto-Transformer requires a 65% tap.

Now voltage is reduced to 0.65 normal, and torque $\propto$ (voltage)^2. Hence

$$\text{New Starting Torque} = (0.65)^2 \text{ (standstill torque)}$$

$$\text{Standstill torque} = 3.75 \text{ cm/ph} = 3 \times 3.75 \times 11.03 \text{ Nm total}$$

∴ $$\text{New starting torque} = (0.65)^2 \times 3 \times 3.75 \times 11.03$$

$$= 0.422 \times 124 = 52.3 \text{ Nm}$$

Example 60

A 4-pole 50 Hz 415 V, 3-phase star-connected induction motor takes a no-load power of 1650 watt at power factor 0.25 lagging. On standstill and a line voltage of 100 volt the power taken is 2410 watts at power factor 0.52 lagging. The rotor and stator copper losses are equal. Determine:

(a) the line current and power factor, the speed, the efficiency and the torque when the power factor is maximum,

(b) the stalling torque and the maximum output power, and

(c) the starting torque on 60% rated voltage.

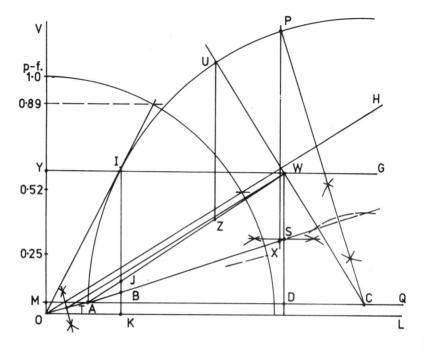

Fig. 60

Solution

This solution demonstrates a 'quadrant' modification of the induction motor current-locus construction which permits a larger scale and so a more accurate diagram. (Ref. Paper 1). The orthodox circle-diagram has no information in the right-hand quadrant which is not available in the left-hand quadrant. It is shown that the latter significant quadrant is easily constructed to a larger scale.

Referring to Figure 60, draw OV ⊥ base line OL, to represent the V-phasor direction. Mark 10 arbitrary units along OV and draw a power-factor quadrant. Working PER PHASE.

Choose a current scale, say 1 cm = 10 amp. Then,

$$\text{power scale} = (\text{phase volts} \times \text{current scale}) = \frac{415 \times 10}{\sqrt{3}}$$

$$= 2400 \text{ watt} = 1 \text{ cm} \quad \text{(vertically)}$$

$$\text{torque scale is, } 1 \text{ cm} = \frac{\text{power scale}}{\text{syn speed in mech rad/sec}}$$

$$= \frac{2400}{2\pi f/p} = \frac{2400 \times 2}{314} = 15.3 \, \text{Nm}$$

From given data,

$$\text{No-load power/ph} = \frac{1650}{3} = 550 \, \text{watt}$$

$$= \frac{550}{2400} \text{ to scale} = 0.23 \, \text{cm} = \text{OM}$$

Draw MQ parallel to OL. Draw OA at p.f. 0.25 lagging on OV, where A is the intercept on MQ. Then OA $= I_0$, the no-load current phasor.

Now at normal voltage,

$$\text{standstill power/phase} = \frac{2410}{3} \left(\frac{415}{100}\right)^2 = 13\,830 \, \text{watt}$$

Average of no-load + standstill phase power

$$= \frac{13\,830 + 550}{2} = 7190 \, \text{watt}, \quad \text{to scale} = 3 \, \text{cm}$$

Comparing with a full circle-diagram construction, we can mark OY = 3 cm along the OV line. Then the point Y is the projection on OV of the centre of the Output Line.

Draw YG parallel to OL.

OH is drawn at power factor 0.52. It is the direction of phasor I_s, but the point I_s may now be off the page owing to the current scale chosen. The point is not required. [Note: in the quadrant construction I_s, I_0 and origin O are three points of a triangle.] Bisect OI_0 at T. Now a line drawn through T, parallel to OI_s, (in our diagram OH), must bisect Output Line I_0I_s. The centre of the Output Line is on YG as shown above, and is determined at W. The lower half of the Output Line, AW, is now drawn.

Draw WC $\perp$ AW to cut AQ at C, the centre of the current-circle locus. The left-hand quadrant of the current locus is now drawn, of radius CA.

The rotor and stator losses are given equal, so WD is bisected at S. WS is now one-half standstill rotor copper loss, (by similar triangles), and AS is the Torque Line.

Part (a). The power factor is a maximum when OI is a tangent to the current circle. By measurement,

current OI at max p.f. = 34.7 amp at p.f. 0.89

Also,

$$\text{since slip} = \frac{\text{rotor cu loss}}{\text{rotor input}}$$

Then

$$\text{Speed} = \frac{IJ}{IB}(1500) = 1372 \text{ r.p.m.}$$

$$\text{Efficiency} = \frac{\text{output power}}{\text{input power}} = \frac{IJ}{IK} = \frac{2.38}{3.06} = 0.778 \text{ or } 77.8\%$$

$$\text{Torque at max p.f.} = 3 \text{ (torque scale)} \times IB = 3 \times 15.3 \times 2.6$$

$$= 119 \text{ Nm for 3 phases.}$$

Part (b)

$$\text{Maximum output} = 3 \text{ (power scale)} \times UZ$$

(where U is WC extended to current circle),

$$= 3 \times 2400 \times 3.26 \text{ watts} \quad \text{for 3 phases}$$

$$= \frac{3 \times 2400 \times 3.26}{746} = 31.5 \text{ hp or } 23.47 \text{ kW}$$

Draw a line ⊥ AS extended, through C to P.

∴   Stalling torque = 3 (torque scale) × PX

$$= 3 \times 15.3 \times 4.4 = 202 \text{ Nm} \quad \text{for 3 phases}$$

(where P is determined by ⊥ from C to AS extended).

Part (c).   Since torque ∝ (voltage)²

Starting Torque on 60% rated voltage

$$= (0.6)^2 \text{ (torque at standstill)}$$

$$= 0.36 \times 2 \, WS \text{ per phase}$$

$$= 3 \times 0.36 \times 2 \times 1.38 \text{ cm} \times 15.3 \quad \text{for 3 phases}$$

$$= 45.6 \text{ Nm}$$

Example 61

A 415 V, 3-phase 50 Hz 8-pole induction motor has a Y-connected stator winding. Stator impedance is $(0.12 + j0.6)$ ohm/phase and for the rotor is $(0.27 + j1.35)$ ohm/phase. The magnetising branch admittance is $(0.0045 - j0.05)$Siemens/phase, referred to the stator. The effective turns ratio per phase, stator/rotor is $1/1.5$. Calculate the supply current, power factor, torque and power developed when the machine is running at 720 rpm.

Solution

$$\text{Synchronous speed} = \frac{60f}{p} = \frac{60 \times 50}{4} = 750 \text{ rpm}$$

Hence loading condition gives slip s,

$$0.04 = \frac{750 - 720}{750}$$

The equivalent circuit/phase is determined as follows;
Rotor impedance/phase referred to stator,

$$= \left(\frac{1}{k}\right)^2 (R_r + jX_r) = \left(\frac{1}{1.5}\right)^2 (0.27 + j1.35)$$

$$= 0.12 + j0.6$$

At slip $= 0.04$, effective rotor resistance, referred to stator,

$$= R_r'/s = \frac{0.12}{0.04} = 3 \text{ ohm}$$

Assuming the magnetising branch moved to the supply terminals, an equivalent circuit can be drawn, Fig. 61 (Ref. 4, p. 263)

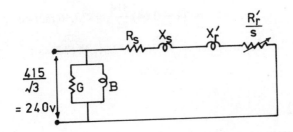

Fig. 61

∴   Total series impedance of stator $= (R_s + R_r'/s) + j(X_s + X_r')$

$$= (0.12 + 3) + j1.2 \text{ ohm}$$

∴ $$I_r' = \frac{240}{(3.12 + j1.2)} = \frac{240(3.12 - j1.2)}{3.12^2 + 1.2^2}$$

$$= \frac{748.8 - j288}{(9.73 + 1.44)} = 67 - j25.78$$

Magnitude of $I_r' = (67^2 + 25.78^2)^{1/2} = 71.85 \text{ amp}$

For the magnetising branch,

$$I_e = V_s G = 240 \times 0.0045 = 1.08$$

$$I_m = jV_s B = 240 \times (-j0.05) = -j12$$

$$\text{Total supply current} = (67 - j25.78) + (1.08 - j12)$$

$$= 68.08 - j37.78$$

$$\text{Magnitude of supply current}, I_s = (68.08^2 + 37.78^2)^{1/2}$$

$$= 77.86$$

$$\text{Input power factor} = \frac{68.08}{77.86} = 0.872 \text{ lagging}$$

$$\text{Now Torque} = \frac{3I_r'^2(R_r'/s)}{\omega_s} = \frac{3 \times (71.85)^2 \times 3}{2\pi f/p}$$

$$= \frac{9 \times 5163.5}{314/4} = 592 \text{ newton metre}$$

and
$$\text{Output power} = \omega_r \textcircled{T}$$

$$\omega_r = (1-s)\omega_s$$

$$= (1 - 0.04)\frac{314}{4} = 75.36 \text{ rad/sec}$$

∴
$$\text{Output power} = 75.36 \times 592 = 44\,613 \text{ watt}$$

$$= 59.8 \text{ hp}$$

Example 62

The load torque on a polyphase induction motor is suddenly increased from zero to a constant value. The combined inertia of motor and load is J and the machine is initially running at a speed close to synchronous. Determine an expression for the transient behaviour of the speed. Comment on the influence of rotor resistance.

Solution

During the transient period, torque supplied by the motor provides inertia torque and load torque. Hence

$$\textcircled{T} = J \, d\omega_r/dt + \textcircled{T}_L$$

Using an approximate expression for torque, (neglecting stator impedance), we have

$$\boxed{T} = \frac{m}{\omega_s k^2} \frac{s^2 V^2}{[R_r^2 + (s\omega L_r)^2]} \frac{R_r}{s}$$

Near synchronous speed, s is very small and $(s\omega L_r)^2 \to 0$. Hence

$$\boxed{T} \simeq \left[\frac{m}{\omega_s k^2} \frac{V^2}{R_r}\right] s = Ks = K(\omega_s - \omega_r)/\omega_s$$

Substituting above,

$$K(\omega_s - \omega_r)/\omega_s = J\, d\omega_r/dt + \boxed{T}_L$$

Rearranging we have,

$$\frac{J\omega_s}{K} \frac{d\omega_r}{dt} + \omega_r = \omega_s - \frac{\boxed{T}_L \omega_s}{K}$$

This is a first-order differential equation with constant coefficients. Then,

$$\text{steady-state } \omega_r = \omega_s - \frac{\boxed{T}_L \omega_s}{K}$$

Hence

$$\omega_r = \omega_s - \frac{\boxed{T}_L \omega_s}{K} + A\,\epsilon^{-t/T_m}$$

Now at $t = 0$, $\omega_r \simeq \omega_s$

$$\omega_s = \omega_s - \frac{T_L \omega_s}{K} + A$$

$$\therefore \qquad A = \frac{\boxed{T}_L \omega_s}{K}$$

Hence

$$\omega_r = \omega_s - \boxed{T}_L \frac{\omega_s}{K}(1 - \epsilon^{-t/T_m})$$

where

$$T_m = J\omega_s/K \text{ sec}$$

Note that $K \propto 1/R_r$. Hence with low R_r there is a smaller speed change for a change in load. Also, the machine adjusts rapidly to the new speed, (viz. $T_m = J\omega_s/K$). With an energy-storing load an oscillatory hunt can occur in steady-state speed, (e.g. a compressor).

Example 63

Approximation in performance prediction for a polyphase induction motor may be used if the ratio of the impedance, due to stator resistance and leakage reactance, to the magnetising impedance, (i) can be approximated to

a small real value, or (ii) is negligible. The approximation is demonstrated for rotor current and torque at starting for a 220 V 50 Hz Y-connected 4 pole induction motor having the following parameters, per phase in ohms;
$R_m = 94.3$, $X_m = 6.0$, $R_1 = 0.063$, $X_1 = 0.12$, $a^2 R_2 = 0.083$,
$a^2 X_2 = 0.12$ and $a =$ transformation ratio, $N_1/N_2 = 2.0$

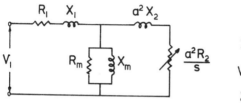
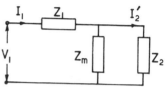

Fig. 63

Solution

It is shown in conventional theory, (Refs. 2, 4 and 6), that the equivalent circuit/phase, referred to the stator, may be drawn as in Fig. 63(a). A simplified schematic circuit can be drawn, Fig. 63(b). Hence,

$$V_1 = I_1 \left(Z_1 + \frac{Z_m Z_2}{Z_m + Z_2} \right)$$

and

$$I_1 = \frac{V_1(Z_m + Z_2)}{Z_1 Z_m + Z_1 Z_2 + Z_2 Z_m}$$

Referred rotor current,

$$I_2' = \frac{V_1 - I_1 Z_1}{Z_2}$$

$$= \frac{V_1}{Z_2} - \frac{V_1 Z_1(Z_2 + Z_m)}{Z_2(Z_1 Z_m + Z_1 Z_2 + Z_2 Z_m)}$$

$$= \frac{V_1 Z_2 Z_m}{Z_2(Z_1 Z_m + Z_2 Z_m + Z_1 Z_2)}$$

$$= \frac{V_1 Z_m}{Z_1 Z_m + Z_2 Z_m + Z_1 Z_2} = \frac{V_1}{Z_1 + Z_2[1 + (Z_1/Z_m)]}$$

If Z_1/Z_m is approximated to a small real value $= c$

$\therefore$

$$I_2' = \frac{V_1}{Z_1 + Z_2(1 + c)}$$

Substituting for Z_1 and Z_2,

$$I_2' = \frac{V_1}{R_1 + jX_1 + a^2[(R_2/s) + jX_2](1 + c)}$$

Rearranging the terms,

$$I_2' = \frac{V_1}{[R_1 + (a^2R_2/s)(1 + c)] + j[X_1 + a^2X_2(1 + c)]}$$

The magnitude of the rotor current (referred to stator),,

$$|I_2'| = \frac{V_1}{\{[R_1 + (a^2R_2/s)(1 + c)]^2 + [X_1 + a^2X_2(1 + c)]^2\}^{1/2}}$$

Now, the input power to the rotor can be expressed/phase;

$$(I_2')^2 \frac{a^2R_2}{s} = (I_2')^2a^2R_2 + (I_2')^2a^2R_2 \frac{(1 - s)}{s}$$

$$= \text{Rotor cu loss} + \text{gross mech power/phase}$$

$$\text{Mech power output} = \omega_R \text{T} \text{ for three phases}$$

$\therefore$
$$\text{T}_{ph} = \frac{1}{\omega_R} (I_2')^2a^2R_2 \frac{(1 - s)}{s}$$

But
$$\omega_R = (1 - s)\omega_s \quad \text{and} \quad 1/\omega_s = (1 - s)/\omega_R$$

Thus we can write

$$\text{T}_{ph} = \frac{V_1^2a^2R_2/s\omega_s}{[R_1 + (a^2R_2/s)(1 + c)]^2 + [X_1 + a^2X_2(1 + c)]^2}$$

If c is negligible it may be eliminated from the expressions for current and torque.

Numerical part: With the given data,

$$|Z_1| = [(0.063)^2 + (0.12)^2]^{1/2} = [(39.6 + 144) \times 10^{-4}]^{1/2}$$

$$= (183.6 \times 10^{-4})^{1/2} = 13.55 \times 10^{-2}$$

$$= 0.136$$

$$Y_m = \frac{1}{R_m} - \frac{j}{X_m} = \frac{1}{94.3} - j\tfrac{1}{6} = 0.0106 - j0.166$$

$$= 0.167\underline{/-86°22'}$$

$\therefore$ $|Z_m| = 5.99 \simeq 6.0$

$$\therefore \qquad c = \frac{|Z_1|}{|Z_m|} = \frac{0.136}{6.0} = 0.0226$$

Now,

$$(R_1 + a^2R_2)^2 = (0.063 + 0.083)^2 = (0.146)^2$$

$$= 0.0213$$

$$(X_1 + a^2X_2)^2 = (0.12 + 0.12)^2 = (0.24)^2$$

$$= 0.0576$$

$$[R_1 + a^2R_2(1 + c)]^2 = [0.063 + 0.083(1.0226)]^2$$

$$= (0.148)^2 = 0.0219$$

$$[X_1 + a^2X_2(1 + c)]^2 = [0.12 + 0.12(1.0226)]^2$$

$$= (0.243)^2 = 0.059$$

(i) *Allowing for c*

At start $s = 1.0$; also $\omega_s = 2\pi f/p = 50\pi$

Denominator for $|I_2'| = (0.0219 + 0.059)^{1/2} = 0.284$

$$\therefore \qquad |I_2'| = \frac{V_1}{0.284} = \frac{220}{\sqrt{3} \times 0.284} = 447\,\text{A}$$

$$\textcircled{T}_{ph} = \frac{(I_2')^2 a^2 R_2}{\omega_s} = \frac{(447)^2 \times 0.083}{50\pi} = 105.5\,\text{Nm}$$

$$\textcircled{T}_{3\,\text{phases}} = 316.5\,\text{Nm}$$

(ii) *Where c is negligible*

Denominator for $|I_2'| = (0.0213 + 0.0576)^{1/2} = 0.28$

$$\therefore \qquad |I_2'| = \frac{V_1}{0.28} = \frac{220}{\sqrt{3} \times 0.28} = 454\,\text{A}$$

$$\textcircled{T}_{ph} = \frac{(454)^2 \times 0.083}{50\pi} = 108.5$$

$$\textcircled{T}_{3\,\text{phases}} = 325.5\,\text{Nm}$$

Since $I_2' = I_2/a$ then

$$\text{Rotor Current} = 2 \times 447 = 894\,\text{A} \quad \text{(i)}$$

$$= 2 \times 454 = 908\,\text{A} \quad \text{(ii)}$$

Example 64

It can be shown that the transient inductance per phase of a 3-phase induction motor can be expressed, $L' = L_{11} - (L_{12}^2/L_{22})$ in transformer notation, (neglecting resistance); the statement can be related to the equivalent circuit/phase expressed in leakage inductances.

Using this approximation, it is required to determine the starting-current transient for a 220 V, 50 Hz, 3 phase Y-connected induction motor having the following constants, referred to the stator/phase; $R_S = 0.4$ ohm, $R_R = 0.6$ ohm, $L_S = 0.03$ H, $L_R = 0.04$ H, $L_0 = 0.03$ H.

Solution

First part.   At start, the rotor is on s/c, (Fig. 64(a)). Hence we have, in operational notation, $(p = \mathrm{d}/\mathrm{d}t)$,

$$V_S = L_{11}pi_1 + L_{12}pi_2$$

$$V_R = L_{22}pi_2 + L_{12}pi_1 = 0 \quad \text{due to the s/c}$$

$$\therefore \qquad pi_2 = -\frac{L_{12}}{L_{22}}pi_1$$

Substitute in expression for V_S,

$$V_S = L_{11}pi_1 - \frac{L_{12}^2}{L_{22}}pi_1 = \left(L_{11} - \frac{L_{12}^2}{L_{22}}\right)pi_1$$

Thus,

$$L' = \left(L_{11} - \frac{L_{12}^2}{L_{22}}\right)$$

If we work in terms of leakage reactances, (Fig. 64(b)), neglecting resistances;

$$\text{Input inductance } L = L_S + \frac{L_0 L_R}{L_0 + L_R}$$

Now $L_S = (L_{11} - L_{12})$ and $L_R = (L_{22} - L_{12})$, also $L_0 = L_{12}$. Then

$$\text{input } L = L_{11} - L_{12} + \frac{L_{12}(L_{22} - L_{12})}{L_{12} + L_{22} - L_{12}}$$

$$= L_{11} - L_{12} + \frac{L_{12}L_{22} - L_{12}^2}{L_{22}}$$

$$= \left(L_{11} - \frac{L_{12}^2}{L_{22}}\right) = L' \quad \text{as given}$$

Second part.   With the given numerical values,

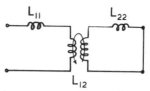

(a) EQUIVALENT CIRCUIT/PHASE.

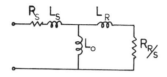

(b) EQUIVALENT CIRCUIT/PHASE.

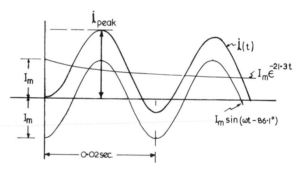

(c) STARTING CURRENT TRANSIENT (APPROX).

Figs. 64 (a, b, c)

$$L_{11} = L_S + L_{12} = L_S + L_0 = 0.03 + 0.03 = 0.06\,H$$

$$L_{12} = L_0 = 0.03\,H$$

Hence,

$$L_{22} = L_R + L_{12} = L_R + L_0 = 0.04 + 0.03 = 0.07\,H$$

$$L' = \left(L_{11} - \frac{L_{12}^2}{L_{22}}\right) = 0.06 - \frac{(0.03)^2}{0.07}$$

$$= 0.06 - \frac{0.0009}{0.07} = 0.06 - 0.013$$

$$= 0.047\,H$$

Also,

$$R = R_S + R_R = 0.4 + 0.6 = 1.0\ \text{ohm} \quad \text{(at starting)}$$

(Alternatively,

$$L' = L_S + \frac{L_0 L_R}{L_0 + L_R} = 0.03 + \frac{0.03 \times 0.04}{0.03 + 0.04}$$

$$= 0.03 + 0.017 = 0.047 \, \text{H})$$

The equivalent circuit reduces to R and L' in series. With the sudden application of sinusoidal emf, $V_m \sin \omega t$ (for the reference phase), i_t is obtained, (Ref. 2, p. 19)

$$i_t = I_m [\epsilon^{-t/T} \sin \phi + \sin (\omega t - \phi)]$$

where

$$I_m = \frac{V_m}{(R^2 + \omega^2 L^2)^{1/2}} = \frac{\sqrt{2} \times (220/\sqrt{3})}{\{1^2 + (314 \times 47 \times 10^{-3})^2\}^{1/2}}$$

$$= \frac{180}{\{1 + (14.7)^2\}^{1/2}} = \frac{180}{(1 + 216)^{1/2}} = \frac{180}{14.8}$$

$$= 12.16 \quad \text{say} \quad 12.2 \, \text{amp}$$

$$\phi = \tan^{-1} \frac{\omega L}{R} = \tan^{-1} 14.7 = 86.1°$$

$$T = \frac{L}{R} = \frac{0.047}{1} = 0.047 \, \text{sec}; \quad \frac{1}{T} = \frac{1}{0.047} = 21.3$$

Hence,

$$i_t = 12.2 [\epsilon^{-21.3t} \sin 86.1° + \sin (\omega t - 86.1°)]$$

$$= 12.2 [\epsilon^{-21.3t} + \sin (\omega t - 86.1°)]$$

$$\text{Approx } i_{\text{peak}} = 12.2(\epsilon^{-0.21} + 1) = 12.2(0.81 + 1)$$

$$= 22.0 \, \text{amp}$$

[assumed to occur about when $\sin (\omega t - 86.1°)$ is maximum, that is, $\omega t \simeq 180°$ and $t = 0.01$ sec on 50 Hz supply.]

See Fig. 64(c).

Chapter Six
Networks

Example 65

Feeders arranged as a ring system supply 3 loads from a substation S. The loads are 150 A at 0.8 p.f. lagging, 100 A at 1.0 p.f., and 200 A at 0.9 p.f. lagging, at points A, B and C respectively. The section feeders have impedances $Z_{SA} = (1 + j3)$ ohm, $Z_{AB} = (2 + j6)$ ohm, $Z_{BC} = (1.5 + j5)$ ohm and $Z_{CS} = (1 + j4)$ ohm. It is required to calculate the current in each feeder section and the volt drop from S to the load point of lowest supply voltage.

Solution

The system may be represented by a single line diagram

Assume

Now,
$$I_{SA} = I_p + jI_q$$
$$I_A = 150(0.8 - j0.6) = 120 - j90$$
$$I_B = 100(1.0 - j0) = 100 - j0$$
$$I_C = 200(0.9 - j0.435) = 180 - j87$$

Hence,
$$I_{AB} = I_{SA} - I_A = (I_p - 120) + j(I_q + 90)$$
$$I_{BC} = I_{AB} - I_B = (I_p - 220) + j(I_q + 90)$$
$$I_{CS} = I_{BC} - I_C = (I_p - 400) + j(I_q + 177)$$

Since the supply voltage is common at S, the overall volt drop, S → S, is zero. In general, a section volt drop may be expressed,
$$(I_1 + jI_2)(R + jX) = (I_1 R - I_2 X) + j(I_2 R + I_1 X)$$

The sum of the real components of volt drop,
$$\Sigma (I_1 R - I_2 X) = [I_p - 3I_q] + [2(I_p - 120) - 6(I_q + 90)] + [1.5(I_p - 220)$$
$$- 5(I_q + 90)] + [1(I_p - 400) - 4(I_q + 177)] = 0$$

Collecting terms,
$$5.5I_p - 18I_q = 2668 \tag{1}$$

The sum of the j-components of volt drop

$$\Sigma\,(I_2R + I_2X) = [I_q + 3I_p] + [2(I_q + 90) + 6(I_p - 120)] + [1.5\,(I_q + 90)$$
$$+ 5(I_p - 220)] + [1(I_q + 177) + 4(I_p - 400)] = 0$$

Collecting terms,
$$18I_p + 5.5I_q = 2928 \tag{2}$$

$$\begin{array}{l|l} (1)\times 5.5 & \overline{30.25I_p - 99I_q = 14\,674} \\ (2)\times 18 & 324.0I_p + 99I_q = 52\,704 \end{array}$$

$$354.25I_p = 67\,378$$

$$I_p = 190.2$$

From (2)
$$5.5I_q = 2928 - (18 \times 190.2) = -495.6$$

$$I_q = -90.1$$

Hence the section currents are obtained,

$$I_{SA} = 190.2 - j90.1$$

$$I_{AB} = 70 - j0.1$$

$$I_{CB} = 29.8 + j0.1 \quad \text{(note reversal of direction)}$$

$$I_{SC} = 209.8 - j86.9$$

Hence the load at B is at the lowest supply voltage.

Note: the section current magnitudes are; SA, 210.42 amp, AB, 70 amp, CB, 29.8 amp, SC, 227.09 amp. These values indicate the saving in conductor section obtained by using a ring circuit, as opposed to a radial supply system.

Second part: Volt drops,

$$V_{SA} = (190.2 - j90.1)(1 + j3)$$

$$= 460.5 + j480.5$$

$$V_{AB} = (70 - j0.1)(2 + j6)$$

$$= 140.6 + j419.8$$

Then
$$V_{SB} = 601.1 + j900.3$$

$$= 1082.5\underline{/56.26^\circ} = \text{Maximum voltage drop}$$

Example 66

A synchronous generator, represented as a source of constant voltage in series with an inductive reactance, X_1, is connected to a load described as a fixed inductive reactance, X_2 in parallel with a variable resistance, R. It is required to show that maximum power is delivered when,

$$\frac{1}{R} = \left(\frac{1}{X_1} + \frac{1}{X_2}\right)$$

Solution

Let generator voltage = V. Then current supplied by generator,

$$I_g = \frac{V}{\left(jX_1 + \dfrac{jX_2 R}{R + jX_2}\right)}$$

Power output = real part of VI_g = Re VI_g

$$= \text{Re } V^2 \left(\frac{R + jX_2}{jX_1 R - X_1 X_2 + jX_2 R}\right)$$

$$= \text{Re } \frac{V^2(R + jX_2)}{(-X_1 X_2) + jR(X_1 + X_2)}$$

$$= \text{Re } V^2 \left\{\frac{(R + jX_2)[-X_1 X_2 - jR(X_1 + X_2)]}{(-X_1 X_2)^2 + R^2(X_1 + X_2)^2}\right\}$$

$$= \text{Re } \frac{V^2}{(X_1 X_2)^2 + R^2(X_1 + X_2)^2}$$

$$\times [-RX_1 X_2 - jR^2(X_1 + X_2) - jX_1 X_2^2 + R(X_1 X_2 + X_2^2)]$$

Real part,

$$P = \frac{V^2 X_2^2 R}{X_1^2 X_2^2 + R^2(X_1 + X_2)^2}$$

For maximum, $dP/dR = 0$

$$[X_1^2 X_2^2 + R^2(X_1 + X_2)^2] V^2 X_2^2 - V^2 X_2^2 R[2R(X_1 + X_2)^2] = 0$$

∴
$$X_1^2 X_2^2 = R^2(X_1 + X_2)^2$$

$$R^2 = \left[\frac{X_1 X_2}{(X_1 + X_2)}\right]^2$$

Hence,

$$\frac{1}{R} = \left(\frac{1}{X_1} + \frac{1}{X_2}\right) \quad \text{is the condition}$$

Example 67

Two generators, having emfs of E_1 and E_2, and impedances Z_1 and Z_2 respectively, operate in parallel to supply a common load of impedance Z. Determine expressions for the current delivered by each generator using the method of loop currents. Verify the solution using the principle of superposition.

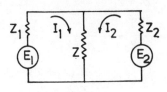

Fig. 67

Solution

Assume loop currents, I_1 and I_2 as shown in Fig. 67. By Kirchhoff's Law,

$$E_1 = (Z_1 + Z)I_1 + ZI_2$$

$$E_2 = ZI_1 + (Z_2 + Z)I_2$$

Solving for I_1 and I_2,

$$I_1 = \frac{E_1(Z_2 + Z) - E_2 Z}{(Z_1 + Z)(Z_2 + Z) - Z^2} = \frac{E_1(Z_2 + Z) - E_2 Z}{Z_1 Z_2 + Z_1 Z + Z_2 Z}$$

$$I_2 = \frac{E_2(Z_1 + Z) - E_1 Z}{Z_1 Z_2 + Z_1 Z + Z_2 Z}$$

By Superposition: First assume $E_2 = 0$. Then

$$I'_G = \frac{E_1}{Z_1 + \dfrac{Z_2 Z}{Z + Z_2}} = \frac{E_1(Z + Z_2)}{Z_1 Z_2 + Z_1 Z + Z_2 Z}$$

Also, current in Z_2 due to I'_G

$$= \frac{Z}{Z_2 + Z} I'_G$$

$$= \frac{Z E_1}{Z_1 Z_2 + Z_1 Z + Z_2 Z} = I'_{Z2}$$

Now, assume $E_1 = 0$, and reinstate E_2,

$$I''_G = \frac{E_2}{Z_2 + \dfrac{Z_1 Z}{Z + Z_1}} = \frac{E_2(Z + Z_1)}{Z_1 Z_2 + Z_1 Z + Z_2 Z}$$

Also, current in Z_1 due to I''_G

$$= \frac{Z}{Z_1 + Z} I''_G$$

$$= \frac{Z E_2}{Z_1 Z_2 + Z_1 Z + Z_2 Z} = I''_{Z1}$$

Hence,

$$I_1 = I'_G - I''_{Z1} = \frac{E_1(Z_2 + Z) - E_2 Z}{Z_1 Z_2 + Z_1 Z + Z_2 Z}$$

$$I_2 = I''_G - I'_{Z2} = \frac{E_2(Z_1 + Z) - E_1 Z}{Z_1 Z_2 + Z_1 Z + Z_2 Z}$$

Example 68

Demonstrate the application of 'node voltages' in the solution of the network problem shown in Fig. 68(a). Hence determine the current supplied to the resistance load in the system shown in Fig. 68(b). Check the numerical solution by Thévénin's method.

Solution

Let V_1, V_2 and V_3 be the potentials of node points as shown in Fig. 68(a). The algebraic sum of currents at each node is zero. Hence we have,

$$\frac{V_1}{Z_2} + \frac{V_1 - E}{Z_1} + \frac{V_1 - V_2}{Z_3} = 0$$

$$\frac{V_2}{Z_4} + \frac{V_2 - V_1}{Z_3} + \frac{V_2 - V_3}{Z_5} = 0$$

$$\frac{V_3}{Z_6} + \frac{V_3 - V_2}{Z_5} = 0$$

We can rearrange these equations and express in terms of admittances, viz;

$$(Y_1 + Y_2 + Y_3)V_1 - Y_3 V_2 = E Y_1$$

$$- Y_3 V_1 + (Y_3 + Y_4 + Y_5)V_2 - Y_5 V_3 = 0$$

$$- Y_5 V_2 + (Y_5 + Y_6)V_3 = 0$$

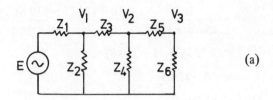

(a)

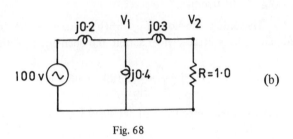

(b)

Fig. 68

These equations are solved to determine V_1, V_2 and V_3. Where there are several nodes, determinants may be used in the solution, as demonstrated below.

Numerical part: Summing the currents at each node (Fig. 68(b)),

$$\frac{V_1}{j0.4} + \frac{V_1 - 100}{j0.2} + \frac{V_1 - V_2}{j0.3} = 0$$

$$\frac{V_2}{1} + \frac{V_2 - V_1}{j0.3} = 0$$

Multiplying both equations by j,

$$(2.5 + 5 + 3.3)V_1 - 3.3V_2 = 500$$

$$-3.3V_1 + (j1.0 + 3.3)V_2 = 0$$

Collecting terms,

$$10.8V_1 - 3.3V_2 = 500$$

$$-3.3V_1 + (j1.0 + 3.3)V_2 = 0$$

Using determinants and Cramer's Rule,

$$V_2 = \frac{\begin{vmatrix} 10.8 & 500 \\ -3.3 & 0 \end{vmatrix}}{\begin{vmatrix} 10.8 & -3.3 \\ -3.3 & (j1.0 + 3.3) \end{vmatrix}} = \frac{1650}{35.64 + j10.8 - 10.89}$$

$$= \frac{1650}{24.75 + j10.8} = \frac{1650(24.75 - j10.8)}{(24.75^2 + 10.8^2)}$$

$$= 2.265(24.75 - j10.8)$$

$$= 56 - j24.3$$

Hence
$$|V_2| = 61.0 \text{ volt}$$
$$|I_R| = 61.0 \text{ amp}$$

Check by Thévenin's Method (Fig. 68(b)). Assume the load resistance removed. Then, by voltage divider action, the open-circuit voltage at the load point,

$$E' = \left(\frac{0.4}{0.4 + 0.2}\right)100 = 66.6 \text{ volt}$$

With E short-circuited, impedance of net viewed at O.C. terminals,

$$Z_{\text{net}} = j0.3 + j\left(\frac{0.2 \times 0.4}{0.2 + 0.4}\right)$$

$$= j0.3 + j0.133 = j0.433$$

When the load is replaced,

$$I_R = \frac{E'}{Z_{\text{net}} + Z_{\text{load}}} = \frac{66.6}{1 + j0.433}$$

$$= \frac{66.6(1 - j0.433)}{1 + (0.433)^2} = \frac{66.6 - j28.8}{1.188}$$

$$= 56 - j24.3$$

Hence
$$|I_R| = (56^2 + 24.3^2)^{1/2} = 61.0 \text{ amp} \quad \text{(as before)}$$

Example 69

A common-emitter transistor amplifier may be represented by an equivalent-T circuit as shown in Figure 69. Determine:

(a) expressions for (i) the voltage, current and power gains, and (ii) the output resistance.

(b) Hence calculate the voltage gain given the following values; $r_b = 100\,\Omega$, $r_d = 5 \times 10^4\,\Omega$, $r_e = 45\,\Omega$, $r_m = 9.5 \times 10^5\,\Omega$, $R_L = 10\,\text{k}\Omega$.

Solution

Part (a)(i).   In terms of the voltages and currents shown,

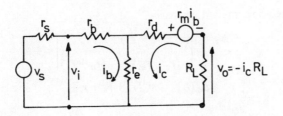

Fig. 69

$$v_i = (r_b + r_e)i_b + r_e i_c$$

$$0 = (r_e - r_m)i_b + (r_d + r_e + R_L)i_c$$

The circuit determinant can be written,

$$\Delta_1 = \begin{vmatrix} (r_b + r_e) & r_e \\ (r_e - r_m) & (r_d + r_e + R_L) \end{vmatrix}$$

Thus

$$\Delta_1(i_b) = \begin{vmatrix} v_1 & r_e \\ 0 & (r_d + r_e + R_L) \end{vmatrix}$$

and

$$i_b = \frac{v_i(r_d + r_e + R_L)}{\Delta_1}$$

Similarly,

$$i_c = \frac{v_i(r_m - r_e)}{\Delta_1}$$

Hence

$$\text{Current Gain}, A(i) = \frac{i_c}{i_b} = \frac{(r_m - r_e)}{(r_d + r_e + R_L)}$$

Now

$$\text{Voltage Gain} = A(v) = \frac{v_0}{v_i} = \frac{-i_c R_L}{v_i}$$

Substituting for i_c from above, we get,

$$A(v) = \frac{-R_L(r_m - r_e)}{\Delta_1} = \frac{-R_L(r_m - r_e)}{(r_b + r_e)(r_d + r_e + R_L) - r_e(r_e - r_m)}$$

Then

$$\text{Power Gain}, A(P) = A(i) \times A(v)$$

Part (a)(ii).   For the output resistance, open-circuit the load, R_L, and short-circuit v_s, (i.e., $v_s = 0$), but include r_s. Now,

$$0 = (r_s + r_b + r_e)i_b + r_e i_c$$

$$v_0 = (r_e - r_m)i_b + (r_d + r_e)i_c$$

Expressed as a determinant, we have

$$\Delta_2 = \begin{vmatrix} (r_s + r_b + r_e) & r_e \\ (r_e - r_m) & (r_d + r_e) \end{vmatrix}$$

Then

$$\Delta_2(i_c) = v_0(r_s + r_b + r_e)$$

Now

$$r_0 = v_0/i_c \qquad \therefore \quad r_0 = \frac{\Delta_2}{(r_s + r_b + r_e)}$$

i.e. Output Resistance,

$$r_0 = \frac{(r_s + r_b + r_e)(r_d + r_e) - r_e(r_e - r_m)}{(r_s + r_b + r_e)}$$

$$= r_d + r_e - r_e \left(\frac{r_e - r_m}{r_s + r_b + r_e} \right)$$

Part (*b*).   Substituting the given numerical values,

$$\text{Voltage gain, } A(v) = \frac{-10 \times 10^3 (9.5 \times 10^5 - 45)}{(100 + 45)(5 \times 10^4 + 45 + 10 \times 10^3) - 45(45 - 9.5 \times 10^5)}$$

$$= \frac{-10^9 \times 9.5}{(145)(6 \times 10^4) - 45(45 - 9.5 \times 10^5)} = \frac{-95 \times 10^4}{870 + 4275}$$

$$= -185$$

N.B.   The minus sign indicates a $180°$ phase shift.

Example 70

Show that an unbalanced star-connected network of n impedances $Z_1, Z_2,$ $\ldots, Z_n$, can be replaced by an equivalent network of impedances, $Z_{12}, Z_{13},$ $\ldots Z_{23}, Z_{24}, \ldots$ etc., joining all the pairs of terminals, excluding the star-point. Hence determine:

(a) the mesh equivalent impedances of a star-connected network in the 3-phase case,

(b) the star equivalent of a mesh network.

Solution

This is known as 'The General Network Theorem'. Let the potentials of the n terminals be V_1, V_2, etc. and for the star-point be V_0.

Then

$$I_1 = (V_1 - V_0)/Z_1, \quad I_2 = (V_2 - V_0)/Z_2, \quad \text{etc.}$$

The star-point O is insulated and thus the sum of the currents must be zero.

$$\therefore \qquad \Sigma I_1 = \Sigma \left[\frac{(V_1 - V_0)}{Z_1}\right] = \Sigma \frac{V_1}{Z_1} - V_0 \Sigma \frac{1}{Z_1} = 0$$

$$\therefore \qquad V_0 = \frac{\Sigma V_1 Z_1^{-1}}{\Sigma Z_1^{-1}}$$

We can write

$$I_1 = V_1 Z_1^{-1} - \frac{\Sigma V_1 Z_1^{-1}}{Z_1 \Sigma Z_1^{-1}}$$

$$= \frac{1}{Z_1 \Sigma Z_1^{-1}} [V_1 \Sigma Z_1^{-1} - (V_1 Z_1^{-1} + V_2 Z_2^{-1} + \ldots + V_n Z_n^{-1})]$$

$$= \frac{1}{Z_1 \Sigma Z_1^{-1}} \left[V_1 \left(\frac{1}{Z_1} + \frac{1}{Z_2} + \ldots + \frac{1}{Z_n}\right) - \left(\frac{V_1}{Z_1} + \frac{V_2}{Z_2} + \ldots + \frac{V_n}{Z_n}\right) \right]$$

$$= \frac{1}{Z_1 \Sigma Z_1^{-1}} \left[\frac{(V_1 - V_2)}{Z_2} + \frac{(V_1 - V_3)}{Z_3} + \ldots + \frac{(V_1 - V_n)}{Z_n} \right]$$

$$= \frac{(V_1 - V_2)}{Z_1 Z_2 \Sigma' Z_1^{-1}} + \frac{(V_1 - V_3)}{Z_1 Z_3 \Sigma Z_1^{-1}} + \ldots + \frac{(V_1 - V_n)}{Z_1 Z_n \Sigma Z_1^{-1}}$$

This would also be the current I_1 for a network of impedances,

$$Z_{12} = Z_1 Z_2 \Sigma Z_1^{-1}$$

$$Z_{13} = Z_1 Z_3 \Sigma Z_1^{-1}, \quad \text{etc.}$$

Therefore for the 3-phase mesh-connection derived from star-connected impedances, Z_1, Z_2 and Z_3 we have (see Figure 70),

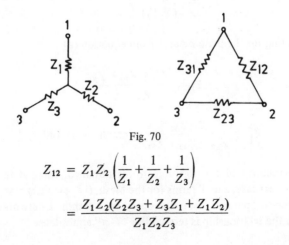

Fig. 70

$$Z_{12} = Z_1 Z_2 \left(\frac{1}{Z_1} + \frac{1}{Z_2} + \frac{1}{Z_3}\right)$$

$$= \frac{Z_1 Z_2 (Z_2 Z_3 + Z_3 Z_1 + Z_1 Z_2)}{Z_1 Z_2 Z_3}$$

$$= \frac{Z_2 Z_3 + Z_3 Z_1 + Z_1 Z_2}{Z_3}$$

Similarly,

$$Z_{23} = \frac{Z_2 Z_3 + Z_3 Z_1 + Z_1 Z_2}{Z_1}$$

$$Z_{31} = \frac{Z_2 Z_3 + Z_3 Z_1 + Z_1 Z_2}{Z_2}$$

N.B. By inverting the Z expressions, and dividing the numerator and denominator of the right-hand expressions by $Z_1 Z_2 Z_3$, we obtain,

$$\frac{1}{Z_{12}} = Y_{12} = \frac{Y_1 Y_2}{Y_1 + Y_2 + Y_3} \quad \text{(etc. in cyclic order)} \qquad \text{(a)}$$

which gives the equivalent Mesh values in admittance terms.

(b) Equivalent Star connection for a given Mesh network.

We can multiply each of the above cyclic admittance equations by the missing cyclic term to obtain,

$$\frac{Y_1 Y_2 Y_3}{Y_1 + Y_2 + Y_3} = Y_{12} Y_3 = Y_{23} Y_1 = Y_{31} Y_2$$

Inverting these terms we can say,

$$\frac{Z_{12}}{Y_3} = \frac{Z_{23}}{Y_1} = \frac{Z_{31}}{Y_2} = \frac{Z_{12} + Z_{23} + Z_{31}}{Y_1 + Y_2 + Y_3}$$

$$= \frac{Z_{12} + Z_{23} + Z_{31}}{Z_{12}(Y_1 Y_2)}$$

by substituting for the denominator from equation (a)

$$\therefore \qquad Y_1 = \frac{Z_{12} + Z_{23} + Z_{31}}{Z_{12} Z_{31}}$$

or

$$Z_1 = \frac{Z_{12} Z_{31}}{Z_{12} + Z_{23} + Z_{31}} \quad \text{(etc. in cyclic order)}$$

Note the similarity of the algebraic forms obtained, using Z terms for the Star, (i.e. series) case, and Y terms for the Mesh, (i.e. parallel) case.

The three-component cases also apply to 4-terminal networks, in which application the relationship is termed the "T–π" equivalence.

Example 71

A power system is represented by the equivalent phase-network shown in Fig. 71(a). Calculate the current in the common impedance Z:
  (a) using the method of cyclic currents,
  (b) using the nodal-voltage method,
  (c) by simplification of the network, to suggest (i) solution by Thévénin's method, (ii) solution by the superposition principle.

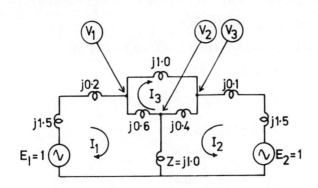

Fig. 71(a)

Solution

Part (a). Neglect all j's initially, to simplify calculations. Mark cyclic currents I_1 and I_2 and I_3 as shown in Fig. 71(a). Applying Kirchhoff's voltage law to the loops,

$$I_1(1.5 + 0.2 + 0.6 + 1) + I_2 - 0.6I_3 = E_1$$

$$I_2(1.5 + 0.1 + 0.4 + 1) + I_1 + 0.4I_3 = E_2$$

$$I_3(0.4 + 0.6 + 1) - 0.6I_1 + 0.4I_2 = 0$$

Rearranging terms,

$$3.3I_1 + I_2 - 0.6I_3 = 1$$

$$I_1 + 3I_2 + 0.4I_3 = 1$$

$$-0.6I_1 + 0.4I_2 + 2I_3 = 0$$

Solve for I_1 and I_2, say by using determinants,

$$I_1 = \frac{\Delta_1}{\Delta} = \frac{\begin{vmatrix} 1 & 1 & -0.6 \\ 1 & 3 & 0.4 \\ 0 & 0.4 & 2 \end{vmatrix}}{\begin{vmatrix} 3.3 & 1 & -0.6 \\ 1 & 3 & 0.4 \\ -0.6 & 0.4 & 2 \end{vmatrix}}$$

$\Delta_1 = 1(3 \times 2 - 0.4 \times 0.4) - 1(1 \times 2 - 0.4 \times 0) + (-0.6)(1 \times 0.4 - 3 \times 0)$

$\quad = 6 - 0.16 - 2 - 0.24 = 3.6$

$\Delta = 3.3(3 \times 2 - 0.4 \times 0.4) - 1\{1 \times 2 - 0.4 \times (-0.6)\}$

$\quad\quad + (-0.6)\{1 \times 0.4 - 3 \times (-0.6)\}$

$\quad = 19.8 - 0.528 - 2 - 0.24 - 0.24 - 1.08 = 15.712$

Hence

$$I_1 = 3.6/15.712 = 0.229$$

$$I_2 = \frac{\begin{vmatrix} 3.3 & 1 & -0.6 \\ 1 & 1 & 0.4 \\ -0.6 & 0 & 2 \end{vmatrix}}{15.76} = \frac{\Delta_2}{\Delta}$$

$\Delta_2 = 3.3(1 \times 2 - 0.4 \times 0) - 1\{1 \times 2 - 0.4 \times (-0.6)\}$

$\quad\quad + (-0.6)\{1 \times 0 - (-0.6) \times 1\}$

$\quad = 6.6 - 2.24 - 0.36 = 4$

$\therefore \quad\quad\quad\quad I_2 = 4/15.71 = 0.255$

Reintroduce j. The network is solely reactive,

$\therefore \quad\quad\quad\quad I_z = I_1 + I_2$

$\quad\quad\quad\quad\quad = -j(0.229 + 0.255) = -j0.484$

Part (*b*).   Mark nodes V_1, V_2 and V_3, Fig. 71(a). Summing nodal currents (and neglecting j's meantime),

$$\frac{V_1 - E_1}{(1.5 + 0.2)} + \frac{V_1 - V_2}{0.6} + \frac{V_1 - V_3}{1} = 0$$

$$\frac{V_2}{1} + \frac{V_2 - V_1}{0.6} + \frac{V_2 - V_3}{0.4} = 0$$

$$\frac{V_3 - E_2}{(1.5 + 0.1)} + \frac{V_3 - V_1}{1} + \frac{V_3 - V_2}{0.4} = 0$$

Rearranging and collecting terms,

$$3.26V_1 - 1.67V_2 - V_3 = 0.59$$

$$-1.67V_1 + 5.17V_2 - 2.5V_3 = 0$$

$$-V_1 - 2.5V_2 + 4.13V_3 = 0.63$$

Solving for V_2, (say by determinants),

$$V_2 = \frac{\Delta_2}{\Delta} = \frac{\begin{vmatrix} 3.26 & 0.59 & -1 \\ -1.67 & 0 & -2.5 \\ -1 & 0.63 & 4.13 \end{vmatrix}}{\begin{vmatrix} 3.26 & -1.67 & -1 \\ -1.67 & 5.17 & -2.5 \\ -1 & -2.5 & 4.13 \end{vmatrix}}$$

$$\Delta_2 = 3.26\{0 \times 4.13 - (-2.5) \times 0.63\} - 0.59\{-1.67 \times 4.13$$

$$-(-2.5)(-1)\} + (-1)\{-1.67 \times 0.63 - 0 \times (-1)\}$$

$$= 5.13 + 4.07 + 1.475 + 1.052 = 11.73$$

$$\Delta = 3.26\{5.17 \times 4.13 - (-2.5)(-2.5)\} - (-1.67)\{(-1.67) \times 4.13$$

$$-(-2.5)(-1)\} + (-1)\{(-1.67)(-2.5) - (5.17)(-1)\}$$

$$= 69.61 - 20.37 - 11.52 - 4.175 - 4.175 - 5.17$$

$$= 24.27$$

$$\therefore\ V_2 = 11.73/24.27 = 0.48$$

Hence

$$I_z = V_2/Z = -j0.48 \quad \text{(reintroducing } j\text{)}$$

Part (c).   The first step in simplification can be to replace the mesh net, between the nodes 1, 2, and 3, by an equivalent star, (see Example 70), with the star point designated '0', Fig. 71(b). Then

$$Z_{10} = \frac{j1 \times j0.6}{j1 + j0.6 + j0.4} = j0.3$$

$$Z_{30} = \frac{j1 \times j0.4}{j1 + j0.6 + j0.4} = j0.2$$

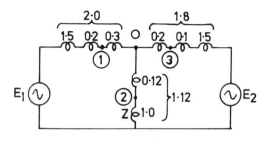

Fig. 71(b)

$$Z_{20} = \frac{j0.6 \times j0.4}{j1 + j0.6 + j0.4} = j0.12$$

and the network is redrawn as in Figure 71(b).

(i)   For the Thévenin solution, assume the Z-shunt branch to be open-circuited, and supplies E_1 and E_2 short-circuited.

Then, viewed from the O.C. terminals,

$$Z_{\text{net}} = j\left(\frac{2.0 \times 1.8}{2.0 + 1.8}\right) = j0.95$$

Replacing Z-branch and voltages E_1 and E_2,

$$I_z = \frac{E_{oc}}{Z_{\text{net}} + Z_{\text{branch}}} = \frac{1}{j(0.95 + 1.12)}$$

$$= -j0.48$$

(ii)   Using the Superposition principle, (Fig. 71(b)). Assume E_2 shorted. Then

$$I'_G = \frac{1}{j\left[2 + \left(\frac{1.8 \times 1.12}{1.8 + 1.12}\right)\right]} = -j0.37$$

Share of this current in Z

$$= I'_z = -j0.37 \times \frac{1.8}{2.92} = -j0.228$$

Now reinstate E_2 but short E_1

$$I''_G = \frac{1}{j\left[1.8 + \left(\frac{2 \times 1.12}{2 + 1.12}\right)\right]} = -j0.397$$

Share of this current in Z

$$= I_z'' = -j0.397 \times \frac{2}{3.12} = -j0.255$$

$$\therefore \quad \text{Current in } Z = I_z' + I_z'' = -j0.483$$

Example 72

The R, Y and B phases of an unbalanced star-connected load are given as resistance of 60 ohm, resistance of 30 ohm and a lossless inductive reactance of 60 ohm respectively. The supply line voltage is 415 volt. Calculate the current in the 60 ohm resistor, using the principle of star-mesh transformation.

Solution. Fig. 72(a)

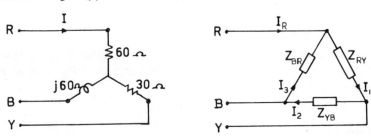

Figs. 72(a, b)

The branch impedances of the mesh equivalent circuit are given as, (see Ex. 70)

$$Z_{RY} = \frac{Z_R Z_Y + Z_Y Z_B + Z_B Z_R}{Z_B} \quad \text{etc.}$$

Using the values given,

$$Z_R Z_Y = 1800, Z_Y Z_B = 1800j, Z_B Z_R = 3600j$$

Thus

$$Z_R Z_Y + Z_Y Z_B + Z_B Z_R = 1800 + j5400 = 1800(1 + j3)$$

Hence

$$Z_{RY} = \frac{1800(1 + j3)}{j60} = -j30(1 + j3) = 90 - j30$$

$$Z_{YB} = \frac{1800(1 + j3)}{60} = 30 + j90$$

$$Z_{BR} = \frac{1800(1 + j3)}{30} = 60 + j180$$

The equivalent mesh circuit can be drawn as in Fig. 72(b). Then

$$I_1 = \frac{415}{90 - j30} = \frac{415}{30}\left(\frac{1}{3 - j1}\right) = \frac{13.83(3 + j1)}{10}$$

$$= 1.383(3 + j1) = 4.149 + j1.383$$

$$I_3 = \frac{(-0.5 + j0.866)415}{60 + j180} = \frac{415(-0.5 + j0.866)}{60(1 + j3)}$$

$$= \frac{6.917(-0.5 + j0.866)(1 - j3)}{10}$$

$$= 0.6917(-0.5 + j0.866 + j1.5 + 2.598)$$

$$= 1.45 + j1.635$$

$$I_R = I_1 - I_3 = 2.699 - j0.252$$

$$= 2.71 \underline{/-5°20'}$$

N.B.   Compare this solution with Example 78. Note that the phase here is with respect to V_{RY} and in Example 78 with respect to V_R, (a phase difference of 30°).

Example 73

A 4-terminal network has the following parameters;

and
$$Z_{oc1} = (1 + j0.5\omega), \quad Z_{oc2} = (2 + j0.5\omega)$$

$$Z_{sc1} = \left(\frac{2 + j1.5\omega}{2 + j0.5\omega}\right)$$

It is required to determine equivalent T- and π-networks; also to check the solution for the π-network by calculating the value for Z_{sc1}. The subscripts 1 and 2 define the input ports, and the impedances are expressed in ohm units.

Solution

Referring to Figure 73

$$Z_{oc1} = 1 + j0.5\omega = Z_a + Z_c$$

$$Z_{oc2} = 2 + j0.5\omega = Z_b + Z_c$$

$$Z_{sc1} = \frac{2 + j1.5\omega}{2 + j0.5\omega} = Z_a + \frac{Z_b Z_c}{Z_b + Z_c}$$

$$= \frac{(2 + j0.5\omega) + j\omega}{2 + j0.5\omega} = 1 + \frac{j\omega}{2 + j0.5\omega}$$

$$= 1 + \frac{2 \times j0.5\omega}{2 + j0.5\omega}$$

$\therefore$ $Z_a = 1.0$ ohm, $Z_b = 2.0$ ohm   and $Z_c = j0.5\omega$ ohm

For the given notation, Figure 73,

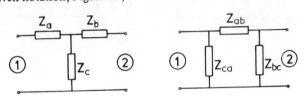

Fig. 73

π-Admittances,

$$Y_{ab} = \frac{Y_a Y_b}{Y_a + Y_b + Y_c}, \quad \text{etc. (in cyclic order).}$$

Now,

$$Y_a Y_b = 1 \times 0.5 = 0.5; \quad Y_b Y_c = 0.5 \times \frac{1}{j0.5\omega} = \frac{1}{j\omega}$$

$$Y_c Y_a = \frac{1}{j0.5\omega} \times 1 = \frac{2}{j\omega}; \quad Y_a + Y_b + Y_c = 1.5 + \frac{2}{j\omega}$$

$\therefore$ $Y_{ab} = \dfrac{0.5}{1.5 + (2/j\omega)}$ and $Z_{ab} = \dfrac{1.5 + (2/j\omega)}{0.5} = 3 + \dfrac{4}{j\omega}$ ohm

$Y_{bc} = \dfrac{(1/j\omega)}{1.5 + (2/j\omega)}$ and $Z_{bc} = \dfrac{1.5 + (2/j\omega)}{1/j\omega} = 2 + j1.5\omega$ ohm

$Y_{ca} = \dfrac{2/j\omega}{1.5 + (2/j\omega)}$ and $Z_{ca} = \dfrac{1.5 + (2/j\omega)}{2/j\omega} = 1 + j0.75\omega$ ohm

Last part

$$Z_{sc1} \text{ (for } \pi) = \frac{[3 + (4/j\omega)](1 + j0.75\omega)}{[3 + (4/j\omega) + 1 + j0.75\omega]} = \frac{Z_{ab} Z_{ca}}{Z_{ab} + Z_{ca}}$$

$$= \frac{(2/j\omega)(2 + j1.5\omega)(1 + j0.75\omega)}{[(4/j\omega) + 1](1 + j0.75\omega)}$$

$$= \frac{(2 + j1.5\omega)}{(2 + j0.5\omega)} \quad \text{as given.}$$

Example 74

A sinusoidal voltage $V_1 = V_m \sin \omega t$ is applied to the network shown in Fig. 74(a). It is required to show that the gain, $|V_2/V_1|$, is unity when $\omega^2 LC = 0$, 1, 2 or 3.

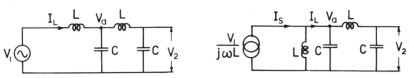

Fig. 74 (a, b)

Solution

We may first substitute a constant current source with a shunt ωL, in place of V_1 and the series ωL, to give an equivalent circuit, Fig. 74(b).

N.B.   The substitution may be justified as follows. In the given figure,

In the new figure,
$$V_a = V_1 - I_L(\omega L)$$
$$V_a = (I_s - I_L)\omega L$$
$$= I_s(\omega L) - I_L(\omega L).$$

Hence V_a is the same in both circuits if $V_1 = I_s(\omega L)$ or $I_s = V_1/\omega L$ and input series (ωL) = new shunt (ωL).

Now the admittance matrix for the new circuit can be stated;

$$
\begin{vmatrix} \dfrac{V_1}{j\omega L} \\[2mm] 0 \end{vmatrix}
=
\begin{vmatrix} \dfrac{1}{j\omega L} + j\omega C + \dfrac{1}{j\omega L} & -\dfrac{1}{j\omega L} \\[2mm] -\dfrac{1}{j\omega L} & \dfrac{1}{j\omega L} + j\omega C \end{vmatrix}
\times
\begin{vmatrix} V_a \\[2mm] V_2 \end{vmatrix}
$$

Then we have;

$$\frac{V_1}{j\omega L} \times \frac{-1}{j\omega L} = \left[\left(\frac{1}{j\omega L}\right)^2 - \left(\frac{1}{j\omega L} + j\omega C\right)\left(\frac{2}{j\omega L} + j\omega C\right)\right] V_2$$

Multiplying across by $(j\omega L)^2$. Hence

$$-V_1 = [1 - (1 - \omega^2 LC)(2 - \omega^2 LC)] V_2$$

$\therefore$
$$\left|\frac{V_2}{V_1}\right| = \frac{1}{-1 + (1 - \omega^2 LC)(2 - \omega^2 LC)}$$

$$= \pm 1 \quad \text{when} \quad \omega^2 LC = 0, 1, 2 \text{ or } 3$$

Example 75

In the given network, Figure 75, each branch has impedance, $Z = j2$ ohm. The supply voltage, $E = 10$ volt. It is required to determine the mesh impedance matrix and the supply current.

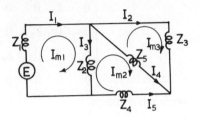

Fig. 75

Solution

Initially branch currents, (I_1, etc.) and mesh currents, (I_{m1}, etc.) are marked on the circuit diagram, with arbitrary directions. The relationships between branch and mesh currents are then expressed in matrix form, viz.,

$$\mathbf{I}_b = \begin{vmatrix} I_1 \\ I_2 \\ I_3 \\ I_4 \\ I_5 \end{vmatrix} = \begin{vmatrix} 1 & 0 & 0 \\ 0 & 0 & 1 \\ 1 & -1 & 0 \\ 0 & 1 & -1 \\ 0 & -1 & 0 \end{vmatrix} \begin{vmatrix} I_{m1} \\ I_{m2} \\ I_{m3} \end{vmatrix} = \mathbf{C}\mathbf{I}_m$$

where $\mathbf{C}$ = transformation matrix.

Similarly we determine by inspection, mesh and branch voltages,

$$\mathbf{V}_m = \begin{vmatrix} V_{m1} \\ V_{m2} \\ V_{m3} \end{vmatrix} = \begin{vmatrix} 1 & 0 & 1 & 0 & 0 \\ 0 & 0 & -1 & 1 & -1 \\ 0 & 1 & 0 & -1 & 0 \end{vmatrix} \begin{vmatrix} V_1 \\ V_2 \\ V_3 \\ V_4 \\ V_5 \end{vmatrix} = \mathbf{C}^t \mathbf{V}_b$$

where this transformation matrix $= \mathbf{C}^t$ and is the transpose of $\mathbf{C}$. Now

$$\mathbf{V}_b = \mathbf{I}_b \mathbf{Z}_b = \mathbf{C}\mathbf{I}_m \mathbf{Z}_b$$
$$\mathbf{V}_m = \mathbf{C}^t \mathbf{V}_b$$

$\therefore$ $\mathbf{Z}_m = \mathbf{C}^t \mathbf{Z}_b \mathbf{C}$

and by inspection of the circuit,

$$= |C^t| \begin{vmatrix} Z_1 & 0 & 0 & 0 & 0 \\ 0 & Z_3 & 0 & 0 & 0 \\ 0 & 0 & Z_2 & 0 & 0 \\ 0 & 0 & 0 & Z_5 & 0 \\ 0 & 0 & 0 & 0 & Z_4 \end{vmatrix} |C|$$

Hence we obtain the mesh relationships,

$$\begin{vmatrix} E \\ 0 \\ 0 \end{vmatrix} = \begin{vmatrix} Z_1 + Z_2 & -Z_2 & 0 \\ -Z_2 & Z_2 + Z_4 + Z_5 & -Z_5 \\ 0 & -Z_5 & Z_3 + Z_5 \end{vmatrix} \times \begin{vmatrix} I_{m1} \\ I_{m2} \\ I_{m3} \end{vmatrix}$$

where the centre matrix is the required mesh impedance matrix, obtained by carrying out the multiplication $\mathbf{C}^t \mathbf{Z}_b \mathbf{C}$.

By neglecting the j's for simplicity and introducing the given numerical values, we can state,

$$10 = 4I_{m1} - 2I_{m2}$$
$$0 = -2I_{m1} + 6I_{m2} - 2I_{m3}$$
$$0 = -2I_{m2} + 4I_{m3}$$

Then

$$I_{m1} = \frac{\begin{vmatrix} 10 & -2 & 0 \\ 0 & 6 & -2 \\ 0 & -2 & 4 \end{vmatrix}}{\begin{vmatrix} 4 & -2 & 0 \\ -2 & 6 & -2 \\ 0 & -2 & 4 \end{vmatrix}} = \frac{200}{64} = 3.125$$

and current from supply $= -j3.125$ amp.

[Assuming $E = (10 + j0)$ volt.]

Example 76

A network arranged as shown in Figure 76 has component values, in ohm unit, as follows; $Z_1 = j10, Z_2 = -j5, Z_3 = j2, Z_4 = -j4, Z_5 = -j10, Z_6 = j5$ an

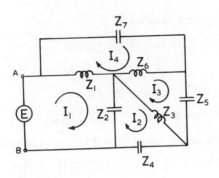

Fig. 76

$Z_7 = -j4$. Using matrix methods, it is required to determine:

(a) the input impedance of the network, measured at terminals A and B,
and

(b) the supply current from a constant voltage supply, $E = (50 + j0)$ volt
applied at these terminals.

Solution. (Ref. 16, p. 204; Ref. 15, p. 75)

Arbitrary mesh currents are marked on the network diagram as shown. By
inspection the mesh matrix equations can be stated;

$$
\begin{vmatrix} E \\ 0 \\ 0 \\ 0 \end{vmatrix} =
\begin{vmatrix}
Z_1+Z_2 & -Z_2 & 0 & -Z_1 \\
-Z_2 & Z_2+Z_3+Z_4 & -Z_3 & 0 \\
0 & -Z_3 & Z_5+Z_3+Z_6 & -Z_6 \\
-Z_1 & 0 & -Z_6 & Z_1+Z_7+Z_6
\end{vmatrix}
\begin{vmatrix} I_1 \\ I_2 \\ I_3 \\ I_4 \end{vmatrix}
$$

Substituting the given values we have, (neglecting the j's),

$$
\begin{vmatrix} 50 \\ \cdot\cdot \\ 0 \\ 0 \\ 0 \end{vmatrix} =
\begin{vmatrix}
5 & . & 5 & 0 & -10 \\
5 & . & -7 & -2 & 0 \\
0 & . & -2 & -3 & -5 \\
-10 & . & 0 & -5 & 11
\end{vmatrix}
\begin{vmatrix} I_1 \\ \cdot\cdot \\ I_2 \\ I_3 \\ I_4 \end{vmatrix}
$$

E and I_1 can be isolated by partitioning as shown by the dotted lines. The
result can be expressed more compactly, viz;

$$
\begin{vmatrix} E \\ \cdot\cdot \\ 0 \end{vmatrix} =
\begin{vmatrix}
Z_{11} & \vdots & Z_{12} \\
\cdots & & \cdots \\
Z_{21} & \vdots & Z_{22}
\end{vmatrix}
\begin{vmatrix} I_1 \\ \cdot\cdot \\ I_2' \end{vmatrix}
$$

Expressed in conventional equations,

$$E = Z_{11}I_1 + Z_{12}I_2'$$

$$0 = Z_{21}I_1 + Z_{22}I_2'$$

$$I_2' = -Z_{21}Z_{22}^{-1}I_1$$

By substitution,

$$E = (Z_{11} - Z_{12}Z_{22}^{-1}Z_{21})I_1$$

Now, substituting numerical values from the partitioned matrix;

$$E = \left| 5 - \begin{bmatrix} 5 & 0 & -10 \end{bmatrix} [Z_{22}^{-1}] \begin{bmatrix} 5 \\ 0 \\ -10 \end{bmatrix} \right| I_1$$

From the matrix Z_{22} we obtain the inverse,

$$Z_{22}^{-1} = \frac{1}{-362} \begin{vmatrix} 58 & -22 & -10 \\ -22 & 77 & 35 \\ -10 & 35 & -17 \end{vmatrix}$$

Hence,

$$Z_{12}Z_{22}^{-1}Z_{21} = -\frac{750}{362}$$

$$\therefore \quad E = \left(5 + \frac{750}{362}\right)I_1 = (5 + 2.07)I_1$$

$$= 7.07I_1$$

Re-introducing the j-operator,

$$Z_{input} = \frac{E}{I_1} = j7.07 \text{ ohm}$$

Part (b).   Given $E = (50 + j0)$,

$$\text{Current from supply}, I_1 = \frac{50 + j0}{j7.07} = -j7.07 \text{ amp}$$

Example 77

Three unequal impedances are connected to form an unsymmetrical 3-phase Y-connected load. It is required:

(a) to show that any one sequence impedance depends on all three of the unequal impedances,

(b) to determine the sequence impedances when the unequal impedances are $Z_R = 120\ \underline{/30^\circ}, Z_Y = 60\ \underline{/-40^\circ}$ and $Z_B = 120\ \underline{/0^\circ}$ in ohm units.

Solution.   (Ref. 16, p. 287)

Unsymmetrical 3-phase phasors are related to the symmetrical positive-, negative-, and zero-sequence components by a transformation matrix, viz;

$$
\begin{vmatrix} I_R \\ I_Y \\ I_B \end{vmatrix} = \begin{vmatrix} 1 & 1 & 1 \\ 1 & \lambda^2 & \lambda \\ 1 & \lambda & \lambda^2 \end{vmatrix} \begin{vmatrix} I_{R0} \\ I_{R1} \\ I_{R2} \end{vmatrix}
$$

where subscripts 0, 1 and 2 refer to zero, positive and negative sequence components respectively.

Symmetrical components are related to unsymmetrical phasors by the inverse matrix, viz;

$$
\begin{vmatrix} V_{R0} \\ V_{R1} \\ V_{R2} \end{vmatrix} = \tfrac{1}{3} \begin{vmatrix} 1 & 1 & 1 \\ 1 & \lambda & \lambda^2 \\ 1 & \lambda^2 & \lambda \end{vmatrix} \begin{vmatrix} V_R \\ V_Y \\ V_B \end{vmatrix}
$$

Using an abbreviated notation, we can express these,

$$[I_{RYB}] = [\lambda][I_{012}]$$

$$[V_{012}] = [\lambda]^{-1}[V_{RYB}]$$

Now,

$$[V_{RYB}] = [Z_{RYB}][I_{RYB}]$$

Transferring from 3-phase to symmetrical components,

$$[V_{012}] = [\lambda]^{-1}[V_{RYB}] = [\lambda]^{-1}[Z_{RYB}][I_{RYB}]$$
$$= [\lambda]^{-1}[Z_{RYB}][\lambda][I_{012}]$$

The matrix product, $[\lambda]^{-1}[Z_{RYB}][\lambda]$ is defined as the 'phase-sequence impedance matrix'.

Expanding the equations for the sequence voltages, we have;

$$
\begin{aligned}
V_{R1} &= \tfrac{1}{3}[(I_{R0}+I_{R1}+I_{R2})Z_R + \lambda(I_{R0}+\lambda^2 I_{R1}+\lambda I_{R2})Z_Y \\
&\quad + \lambda^2(I_{R0}+\lambda I_{R1}+\lambda^2 I_{R2})Z_B] \\
&= \tfrac{1}{3}(Z_R+Z_Y+Z_B)I_{R1} + \tfrac{1}{3}(Z_R+\lambda^2 Z_Y+\lambda Z_B)I_{R2} \\
&\quad + \tfrac{1}{3}(Z_R+\lambda Z_Y+\lambda^2 Z_B)I_{R0} \\
&= I_{R1}Z_0 + I_{R2}Z_2 + I_{R0}Z_1
\end{aligned}
$$

Similarly,

$$V_{R2} = I_{R1}Z_1 + I_{R2}Z_0 + I_{R0}Z_2$$

$$V_{R0} = I_{R1}Z_2 + I_{R2}Z_1 + I_{R0}Z_0$$

The symmetrical impedances can be expressed,

$$Z_0 = \tfrac{1}{3}(Z_R + Z_Y + Z_B)$$

$$Z_1 = \tfrac{1}{3}(Z_R + \lambda Z_Y + \lambda^2 Z_B)$$

$$Z_2 = \tfrac{1}{3}(Z_R + \lambda^2 Z_Y + \lambda Z_B)$$

N.B.   A sequence impedance depends on all three of the unequal impedances. Also, the volt drop of any one sequence depends on the currents of all three sequences.

Commonly in power equipment, where $Z_R = Z_Y = Z_B = $ (say) Z, i.e., a balanced loading, then since $(1 + \lambda + \lambda^2) = 0$,

$$V_{R1} = I_{R1}Z, \quad V_{R2} = I_{R2}Z \quad \text{and} \quad V_{R0} = I_{R0}Z$$

and providing there is no mutual between phases, the symmetrical components of unbalanced currents in balanced Y or series impedances produce volt drops of like sequence only.

If there is no neutral return wire, there can be no zero-sequence component of current, this being a single phase current.

Numerical part.   Given

$$Z_R = 120\underline{/30°}, \quad Z_Y = 60\underline{/-40°}, \quad Z_B = 120 \text{ ohms.}$$

Hence

$$Z_0 = \tfrac{1}{3}(Z_R + Z_Y + Z_B)$$

$$= \tfrac{1}{3}(120\underline{/30°} + 60\underline{/-40°} + 120)$$

$$= (40 \cos 30° + j40 \sin 30°) + (20 \cos 40° - j20 \sin 40°) + 40$$

$$= 34.64 + j20 + 15.32 - j12.85 + 40$$

$$= 89.96 + j7.15$$

$$= [(89.96)^2 + (7.15)^2]^{1/2} \tan^{-1}\left(\frac{7.15}{89.96}\right)$$

$$= 90.24\underline{/4°33'}$$

$$Z_1 = \tfrac{1}{3}(Z_R + \lambda Z_Y + \lambda^2 Z_B)$$

$$= \tfrac{1}{3}(120\underline{/30°} + 60\underline{/-40° + 120°} + 120\underline{/240°})$$

$$= (40 \cos 30° + j40 \sin 30°) + (20 \cos 80° + j20 \sin 80°)$$

$$\quad + (40 \cos 240° + j40 \sin 240°)$$

$$= 34.64 + j20 + 3.473 + j19.7 - 20 - j34.64$$

$$= 18.11 + j5.06$$

$$= [(18.11)^2 + (5.06)^2]^{1/2} \tan^{-1}\left(\frac{5.06}{18.11}\right)$$

$$= 18.8\underline{/15°37'}$$

$$Z_2 = \tfrac{1}{3}(Z_R + \lambda^2 Z_Y + \lambda Z_B)$$

$$= \tfrac{1}{3}(120\underline{/30°} + 60\underline{/-40° + 240°} + 120\underline{/120°})$$

$$= (40 \cos 30° + j40 \sin 30°) + (20 \cos 200° + j20 \sin 200°)$$

$$+ (40 \cos 120° + j40 \sin 120°)$$

$$= (34.64 + j20) + (-18.79 - j6.841) + (-20 + j34.64)$$

$$= -4.15 + 47.8$$

$$= [(4.15)^2 + (47.8)^2]^{1/2} \tan^{-1}\left(\frac{-47.8}{4.15}\right)$$

$$= 48.00\underline{/94°56'}$$

Example 78

A symmetrical 3-phase 3-wire system supplies an unsymmetrical star-connected load. The R, Y and B phases of the load are resistance of 60 ohm, resistance of 30 ohm and a lossless inductive reactance of 60 ohm respectively and the supply line voltage is 415 volt. It is required to calculate the current in the 60 ohm resistor.

Solution

In symmetrical component notation, in general,

$$V_{R1} = I_{R1}Z_0 + I_{R2}Z_2 + I_{R0}Z_1$$

$$V_{R2} = I_{R1}Z_1 + I_{R2}Z_0 + I_{R0}Z_2$$

There is no neutral wire and hence no zero-sequence current. Also the supply is symmetrical. Hence we can write;

$$V_{R1} = I_{R1}Z_0 + I_{R2}Z_2 = 240$$

$$V_{R2} = I_{R1}Z_1 + I_{R2}Z_0 = 0$$

Then,

$$I_{R2} = -\left(\frac{Z_1}{Z_0}\right)I_{R1}$$

and

$$V_{R1} = I_{R1}Z_0 - \left(\frac{Z_2 Z_1}{Z_0}\right) I_{R1}$$

$$I_{R1} = V_{R1}\left(\frac{Z_0}{Z_0^2 - Z_1 Z_2}\right)$$

Now

$$Z_0 = \tfrac{1}{3}(Z_R + Z_Y + Z_B) = \tfrac{1}{3}(60 + 30 + j60)$$

$$= 30 + j20 = 36.04 \underline{/33°41'}$$

$$Z_1 = \tfrac{1}{3}(Z_R + \lambda Z_Y + \lambda^2 Z_B) = 20 + 10(-0.5 + j0.866)$$

$$+ j20(-0.5 - j0.866)$$

$$= 32.32 - j1.34 = 32.35 \underline{/-2°22'}$$

$$Z_2 = \tfrac{1}{3}(Z_R + \lambda^2 Z_Y + \lambda Z_B) = 20 + 10(-0.5 - j0.866)$$

$$+ j20(-0.5 + j0.866)$$

$$= -2.32 - j18.66 = 18.8 \underline{/-97°6'}$$

Using rectangular coordinates,

$$Z_0^2 = (30 + j20)^2 = 500 + j1200$$

$$Z_1 Z_2 = (32.32 - j1.34)(-2.32 - j18.66) = -100 - j600$$

$$Z_0^2 - Z_1 Z_2 = 600 + j1800$$

Substituting in the above expressions,

$$I_{R1} = 240\left(\frac{30 + j20}{600 + j1800}\right) = 4\left(\frac{3 + j2}{1 + j3}\right)$$

$$= 3.6 - j2.8$$

$$I_{R2} = \frac{(32.32 - j1.34)}{(30 + j20)}(3.6 - j2.8)$$

$$= -1.132 + j3.92$$

Then,

$$I_R = I_{R1} + I_{R2} = 2.468 + j1.12$$

$$= 2.71 \underline{/24°40'} \quad \text{(reference phasor } V_R)$$

(Compare this solution with Example 72 where the reference phasor was V_{RY}, i.e., a difference of 30°)

Example 79

An unbalanced star-connected 3-phase source of emf is connected to three star-connected resistances, each of 8 ohm. The source phase voltages are

$V_R = 100$, $V_Y = 120 \underline{/-90°}$ and $V_B = 80 \underline{/150°}$. If the phase sequence is RYB, calculate the current in the resistor in the Y-phase. The load star-point is insulated.

Solution 1

Using the method of symmetrical components and taking phase R as the reference phase,

$$V_{R1} = \tfrac{1}{3}(V_R + \lambda V_Y + \lambda^2 V_B)$$

$$= \tfrac{1}{3}(100 + 120 \underline{/-90° + 120°} + 80 \underline{/150° + 240°}$$

$$= \tfrac{1}{3}[100 + (120 \cos 30° + j120 \sin 30°) + (80 \cos 390° + j80 \sin 390°)]$$

$$= \tfrac{1}{3}[100 + (103.9 + j60) + (69.28 + j40)]$$

$$= \tfrac{1}{3}(273.2 + j100) = 91.1 + j33.3$$

$$V_{R2} = \tfrac{1}{3}(V_R + \lambda^2 V_Y + \lambda V_B)$$

$$= \tfrac{1}{3}(100 + 120 \underline{/-90° + 240°} + 80 \underline{/150° + 120°}$$

$$= \tfrac{1}{3}[100 + (120 \cos 150° + j120 \sin 150°) + (80 \cos 270° + j80 \sin 270°)]$$

$$= \tfrac{1}{3}[100 + (-103.9 + j60) + (0 - j80)] = \tfrac{1}{3}(-3.9 - j20)$$

$$= -1.3 - j6.67$$

Now

$$V_{Y1} = \lambda^2 V_{R1} = (91.1 + j33.3)(-0.5 - j0.866)$$

$$= (-45.55 - j16.65 - j78.89 + 28.84)$$

$$= -16.71 - j95.54$$

$$V_{Y2} = \lambda V_{R2} = (-1.3 - j6.67)(-0.5 + j0.866)$$

$$= (0.65 + j3.33 - j1.126 + 5.78)$$

$$= 6.43 + j2.2$$

The star-connected load is symmetrical,

$$\therefore \qquad I_{Y1} = \frac{-16.71 - j95.54}{8} = -2.09 - j11.94$$

$$I_{Y2} = \frac{6.43 + j2.2}{8} = 0.8 + j0.27$$

Being star-connected and insulated there is no zero-sequence current.

$\therefore$
$$I_Y = I_{Y1} + I_{Y2} = -1.29 - j11.67$$
$$|I_Y| = 11.74 \text{ amp}$$

Solution 2

The phase sequence can be read as *YBR*. Adjusting the given voltages to give *Y* as reference phase (Fig. 79)

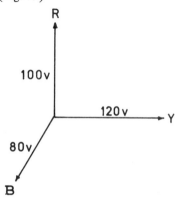

Fig. 79

$$V_Y = 120, \quad V_B = 80\underline{/-120^\circ}, \quad V_R = 100\underline{/90^\circ}$$

We can write,

$$V_{Y1} = \tfrac{1}{3}(V_Y + \lambda V_B + \lambda^2 V_R)$$
$$= \tfrac{1}{3}(120 + 80\underline{/-120^\circ + 120^\circ} + 100\underline{/90^\circ + 240^\circ}$$
$$= \tfrac{1}{3}[120 + 80 + (100\cos 313^\circ + j\sin 313^\circ)]$$
$$= \tfrac{1}{3}(120 + 80 + 86.6 - j50) = \tfrac{1}{3}(286.6 - j50)$$
$$= 95.5 - j16.67$$

$$V_{Y2} = \tfrac{1}{3}(V_Y + \lambda^2 V_B + \lambda V_R)$$
$$= \tfrac{1}{3}(120 + 80\underline{/-120^\circ + 240^\circ} + 100\underline{/90^\circ + 120^\circ})$$
$$= \tfrac{1}{3}[120 + (80\cos 120^\circ + j80\sin 120^\circ) + (100\cos 210^\circ + j100\sin 210^\circ)]$$
$$= \tfrac{1}{3}(120 - 40 + j69.28 - 86.6 - j50) = \tfrac{1}{3}(-6.6 + j19.28)$$
$$= -2.2 + j6.43$$

The star-connected load is symmetrical and there is no zero-sequence component of current. Then

$$I_{Y1} = \frac{95.5 - j16.67}{8} = 11.94 - j2.08$$

$$I_{Y2} = \frac{-2.2 + j6.43}{8} = -0.27 + j0.8$$

$$\therefore \qquad I_Y = I_{Y1} + I_{Y2} = 11.67 - j1.28$$

$$|I_Y| = 11.74 \text{ amp}$$

N.B.   An alternative solution to Solution 1, with R as the reference phasor, may begin by taking,

$$V_{Y1} = \lambda^2 V_{R1} = \tfrac{1}{3}(\lambda^2 V_R + V_Y + \lambda V_B)$$

and

$$V_{Y2} = \lambda V_{R2} = \tfrac{1}{3}(\lambda V_R + V_Y + \lambda^2 V_B)$$

Then substitute given values and proceed as before.

Example 80

A 6600 V, 3-phase synchronous generator has positive, negative and zero-sequence reactances of 4.5, 3.0 and 1.5 ohm/phase respectively. Resistance may be neglected.

(a) Calculate, and illustrate by phasor diagrams, the symmetrical components of fault current when one line is short-circuited to the star point at the terminals of the machine.

(b) Calculate the magnitude of the voltage between either of the other two lines and the star-point under the fault conditions.

Solution

Part (a).   From the given condition, $V_R = 0, I_Y = 0, I_B = 0$. Consider phase R.

$$I_R = I_{R1} + I_{R2} + I_{R0}$$

$$I_{R1} = \tfrac{1}{3}(I_R + \lambda I_Y + \lambda^2 I_B) = \tfrac{1}{3}I_R$$

$$I_{R2} = \tfrac{1}{3}(I_R + \lambda^2 I_Y + \lambda I_B) = \tfrac{1}{3}I_R$$

$$I_{R0} = \tfrac{1}{3}(I_R + I_Y + I_B) = \tfrac{1}{3}I_R$$

Hence the symmetrical components of current can be represented as in Fig. 80.

The synchronous generator is assumed to generate a positive-sequence voltage. Hence the sequence voltages can be expressed,

$$E = I_{R1}Z_{G1} + V_{R1}$$

$$0 = I_{R2}Z_{G2} + V_{R2}$$

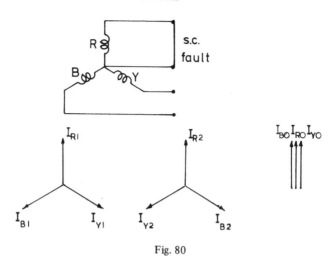

Fig. 80

Then

$$0 = I_{R0}Z_{G0} + V_{R0}$$

Now

$$V_{R2} = -I_{R2}Z_{G2} \quad \text{and} \quad V_{R0} = -I_{R0}Z_{G0}$$

$$V_R = V_{R1} + V_{R2} + V_{R0} = 0$$

$$\therefore \qquad V_{R1} = -V_{R2} - V_{R0}$$

Substituting above,

$$E = I_{R1}Z_{G1} - V_{R2} - V_{R0}$$

But

$$= I_{R1}Z_{G1} + I_{R2}Z_{G2} + I_{R0}Z_{G0}$$

$$I_{R1} = I_{R2} = I_{R0} = \tfrac{1}{3}I_R$$

$$\therefore \qquad 3E = I_R(Z_{G1} + Z_{G2} + Z_{G0})$$

and

$$I_R = \frac{3E}{Z_{G1} + Z_{G2} + Z_{G0}}$$

Substituting numerical values:

$$E = \frac{6600}{\sqrt{3}} = 3810$$

$$I_R = \frac{3 \times 3810}{j4.5 + j3 + j1.5} = \frac{11\,430}{j9} = -j1270$$

Then magnitude of symmetrical components of current

$$= \tfrac{1}{3}(1270) = 423.3 \text{ amp}$$

Part (b). Consider the voltage between the Y line and the star-point under fault conditions;

$$V_Y = V_{Y1} + V_{Y2} + V_{Y0}$$
$$= \lambda^2 V_{R1} + \lambda V_{R2} + V_{R0}$$
$$= \lambda^2(-V_{R2} - V_{R0}) + \lambda V_{R2} + V_{R0}$$

since $V_R = 0$ (above),

$$= (\lambda - \lambda^2) V_{R2} + (1 - \lambda^2) V_{R0}$$
$$= (\lambda^2 - \lambda) I_{R2} Z_{G2} + (\lambda^2 - 1) I_{R0} Z_{G0}$$

Substituting $I_{R2} = I_{R0} = \frac{1}{3} I_R = -j423.3$

$$(\lambda^2 - \lambda) = -j1.732 \quad \text{and} \quad (\lambda^2 - 1) = (-1.5 - j0.866)$$

$$\therefore \qquad V_Y = -j423.3(-j1.732)j3 + (-1.5 - j0.866)j1.5$$
$$= -j423.3(6.496 - j2.25)$$
$$= -952.3 - j2749$$
$$|V_Y| = 2910 \text{ volt}$$

Example 81

A 6600 V, 3-phase Y-connected synchronous generator has positive, negative and zero-sequence reactances of 4.5, 3.0 and 1.5 ohm/phase respectively. Resistance may be neglected. A short-circuit occurs between two lines near the terminals of the machine. Calculate the magnitude of the fault current, and the voltage of the good phase under fault conditions. Give diagrams to illustrate the symmetrical components of fault current and the equivalent sequence network. Comment on the voltages in the faulty phases.

Solution

$$\text{Let } E = \text{emf/phase} = 6600/\sqrt{3} = 3810 \text{ volt.}$$

Take B as the reference phase; sequence can be stated BRY. Conditions due to the fault are Fig. 81(a),

$$I_B = 0; \quad I_R = -I_Y; \quad V_{RY} = 0$$

The isolated star-point means there are no zero-sequence currents. Now

$$I_B = I_{B1} + I_{B2} + I_{B0} = 0$$

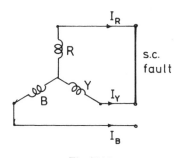

Fig. 81(a)

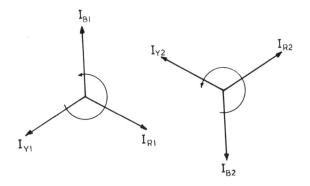

Fig. 81(b)

and thus $I_{B1} = -I_{B2}$ (Fig. 81(b)).

$$I_R = \lambda^2 I_{B1} + \lambda I_{B2}$$
$$= (\lambda^2 - \lambda) I_{B1} = -j\sqrt{3} I_{B1}$$
$$V_{RY} = V_R - V_Y = 0 \quad \text{and thus} \quad V_R = V_Y$$

Substituting for V_R and V_Y in terms of the reference phase,

$$\lambda^2 E - I_{R1} Z_{G1} - I_{R2} Z_{G2} = \lambda E - I_{Y1} Z_{G1} - I_{Y2} Z_{G2}$$
$$\therefore \quad \lambda^2 E - (\lambda^2 I_{B1}) Z_{G1} - (\lambda I_{B2}) Z_{G2} = \lambda E - (\lambda I_{B1}) Z_{G1} - (\lambda^2 I_{B2}) Z_{G2}$$

But $I_{B1} = -I_{B2}$, so we have,

$$E(\lambda^2 - \lambda) = I_{B1}[Z_{G1}(\lambda^2 - \lambda) + Z_{G2}(\lambda^2 - \lambda)]$$

$$\therefore \qquad I_{B1} = \frac{E}{Z_{G1} + Z_{G2}} = \frac{3810}{(j4.5 + j3)} = -j508$$

$$\therefore \qquad |I_R| = \sqrt{3}|I_{B1}| = \sqrt{3} \times 508 = 880 \text{ amp}$$

Now

$$V_B = E - I_{B1}Z_{G1} - I_{B2}Z_{G2} = E - I_{B1}Z_{G1} + I_{B1}Z_{G2}$$

$$= E - I_{B1}(Z_{G1} - Z_{G2})$$

$$= 3810 - (-j508)(j1.5) = 3810 - 762$$

$$= 3048 \text{ volt}$$

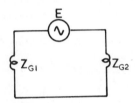

Fig. 81(c)

Note that the 'network' with E, Z_{G1} and Z_{G2} is a mnemonic [Fig. 81(c)] for remembering the fault current equation and represents no physical circuit. Examination of the voltages in the faulty phases may be made as follows:

$$V_{RY} = V_R - V_Y = V_{R1} + V_{R2} + V_{R0} - V_{Y1} - V_{Y2} - V_{Y0}$$

$$= V_{R1} + V_{R2} - V_{Y1} - V_{Y2}$$

$$= \lambda^2 V_{B1} + \lambda V_{B2} - \lambda V_{B1} - \lambda^2 V_{B2}$$

$$= (\lambda^2 - \lambda) V_{B1} + (\lambda - \lambda^2) V_{B2} = 0$$

$$\therefore \qquad V_{B1} = V_{B2}$$

In the negative-sequence circuit, $0 = I_{B2}Z_{G2} + V_{B2}$. But

$$I_{B2} = \frac{-E_B}{Z_{G1} + Z_{G2}}$$

$$\therefore \quad V_{B1} = V_{B2} = \frac{Z_{G2}E_B}{Z_{G1} + Z_{G2}} \quad \text{and hence} \quad V_B = 2\left(\frac{Z_{G2}E_B}{Z_{G1} + Z_{G2}}\right)$$

The sequence voltage vectors at the fault can be drawn, Fig. 81(d)

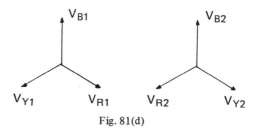

Fig. 81(d)

The phase-voltages at the fault, of the R and Y-phases must be equal as the two terminals are connected. The value of this voltage is obtained,

$$V_R = V_{R1} + V_{R2} = \lambda^2 V_{B1} + \lambda V_{B2} = -V_{B1}$$

$$= -\left(\frac{Z_{G2}}{Z_{G1} + Z_{G2}}\right)E_B$$

$$V_Y = V_{Y1} + V_{Y2} = \lambda V_{B1} + \lambda^2 V_{B2} = -V_{B1}$$

$$= -\left(\frac{Z_{G2}}{Z_{G1} + Z_{G2}}\right)E_B$$

Example 82

Short-circuits occur between the R and Y terminals and the star-point of a 3300 V synchronous generator. The reactances of the windings to positive, negative and zero-sequence currents are 1.2, 0.9 and 0.45 ohm/phase respectively. Calculate the fault current in the R phase and the voltage of the B phase under sustained fault conditions. The phase sequence is given RYB. Draw a network to illustrate the condition.

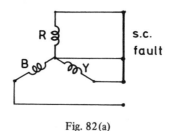

Fig. 82(a)

Solution

Let $E = $ emf/phase $= 3300/\sqrt{3} = 1905$ volt.

Take B as reference phase; sequence can be stated BRY.

Conditions due to the fault are $I_B = 0$, $V_R = V_Y = 0$ (Fig. 82(a)). Now

$$I_B = I_{B1} + I_{B2} + I_{B0} = 0 \tag{1}$$

$$V_R = \lambda^2 E - \lambda^2 I_{B1} Z_{G1} - \lambda I_{B2} Z_{G2} - I_{B0} Z_{G0} = 0 \tag{2}$$

$$V_Y = \lambda E - \lambda I_{B1} Z_{G1} - \lambda^2 I_{B2} Z_{G2} - I_{B0} Z_{G0} = 0 \tag{3}$$

Multiply (3) by λ

$$\lambda^2 E - \lambda^2 I_{B1} Z_{G1} - I_{B2} Z_{G2} - \lambda I_{B0} Z_{G0} = 0 \tag{4}$$

Subtract (4) from (2)

$$(-\lambda + 1) I_{B2} Z_{G2} - (1 - \lambda) I_{B0} Z_{G0} = 0$$

Also, from (1), $I_{B0} = -(I_{B1} + I_{B2})$. Then

$$I_{B2} Z_{G2} = I_{B0} Z_{G0} = -(I_{B1} + I_{B2}) Z_{G0} \tag{5}$$

Hence

$$I_{B2} = -I_{B1} \left(\frac{Z_{G0}}{Z_{G2} + Z_{G0}} \right)$$

Now subtracting (3) from (2) gives,

$$(\lambda^2 - \lambda) E - (\lambda^2 - \lambda) I_{B1} Z_{G1} + (\lambda^2 - \lambda) I_{B2} Z_{G2} = 0$$

$$E = I_{B1} Z_{G1} - I_{B2} Z_{G2}$$

$$= I_{B1} Z_{G1} + I_{B1} \left(\frac{Z_{G0} Z_{G2}}{Z_{G2} + Z_{G0}} \right)$$

Summarising:

$$I_{B1} = \frac{E}{Z_{G1} + [Z_{G0} Z_{G2}/(Z_{G2} + Z_{G0})]}$$

$$I_{B2} = -I_{B1} \frac{Z_{G0}}{(Z_{G2} + Z_{G0})}$$

$$I_{B0} = -I_{B1} \frac{Z_{G2}}{(Z_{G2} + Z_{G0})} \quad \text{from equation (5)}$$

Substituting numerical values, we have,

$$Z_{G0} Z_{G2} = (j0.45)(j0.9) = -0.405$$

$$Z_{G0} + Z_{G2} = j0.45 + j0.9 = j1.35$$

$$\frac{Z_{G0} Z_{G2}}{Z_{G0} + Z_{G2}} = \frac{-0.405}{j1.35} = j0.3$$

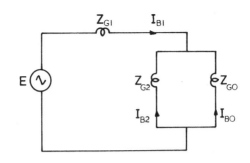

Fig. 82(b)

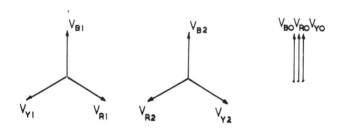

Fig. 82(c)

$$\frac{Z_{G0}}{Z_{G0}+Z_{G2}} = \frac{j0.45}{j1.35} = 0.333 \quad \text{and} \quad \frac{Z_{G2}}{Z_{G0}+Z_{G2}} = 0.666$$

Then,

$$I_{B1} = \frac{1905}{j1.2 + j0.3} = -j1270$$

$$I_{B2} = -(-j1270)(0.333) = j423$$

$$I_{B0} = -(-j1270)(0.666) = j846$$

$$I_{R1} = \lambda^2 I_{B1} = (-0.5 - j0.866)(-j1270) = -1100 + j636$$

$$I_{R2} = \lambda I_{B2} = (-0.5 + j0.866)(j424) = -366 - j212$$

$$I_{R0} = I_{B0} = j846$$

$$\therefore \qquad I_R = \lambda^2 I_{B1} + \lambda I_{B2} + I_{B0} = -1468 + j1270$$

$$|I_R| = 1941 \text{ amp}$$

Now

$$E = I_{B1} Z_{G1} + V_{B1}$$

and

$$V_{B1} = \tfrac{1}{3}(V_B + \lambda V_R + \lambda^2 V_Y) = \tfrac{1}{3}V_B$$

$$V_{B1} = E - I_{B1}Z_{G1} = 1905 - 1524 = 381$$

$$\therefore \qquad |V_B| = 3V_{B1} = 1143 \text{ volt}$$

a mnemonic network can be drawn as in Fig. 82(b).

Example 83

Two 6600 V, 20 MVA, 3-phase synchronous generators operating in parallel have each positive, negative and zero-sequence reactances of 20, 15 and 7 per cent respectively. Assume one machine has the star-point solidly earthed,[*] the other machine is not earthed. Calculate:

(a) the fault current if one busbar is earthed,

(b) the fault current if the earth connection of the star-point has resistance of 0.2 ohm for the same busbar fault. ([*] not always normal practice.)

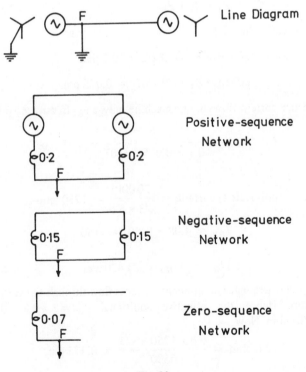

Fig. 83

Solution

(a)   Positive and negative-sequence current are fed to the fault from both machines, in parallel. Zero-sequence currents can flow only in the machine with the earthed star-point. The appropriate sequence-networks will then be as shown, Fig. 83.

Fault conditions give, (with fault on R-busbar)

Now
$$I_Y = I_B = 0 \quad \text{and} \quad V_R = 0$$

$$I_{R0} = \tfrac{1}{3}(I_R + I_Y + I_B) = \tfrac{1}{3}I_R$$

$$I_{R1} = \tfrac{1}{3}(I_R + \lambda I_Y + \lambda^2 I_B) = \tfrac{1}{3}I_R$$

$$I_{R2} = \tfrac{1}{3}(I_R + \lambda^2 I_Y + \lambda I_B) = \tfrac{1}{3}I_R$$

$$\therefore \qquad I_{R0} = I_{R1} = I_{R2} = \tfrac{1}{3}I_R$$

$$V_R = E - (I_{R1}Z_1 + I_{R2}Z_2 + I_{R0}Z_0) = 0$$

$$\therefore \qquad I_{R0} = \frac{E}{Z_1 + Z_2 + Z_0}$$

With two machines in parallel,

$$\text{effective } Z_1 = 0.2/2 = 0.1 \text{ p.u.}$$

$$\text{effective } Z_2 = 0.15/2 = 0.075 \text{ p.u.}$$

Zero-sequence current flows in one machine only, and effective $Z_0 = 0.07$ p.u.

$$\therefore \qquad I_{R0} \text{ (p.u.)} = \frac{1}{0.1 + 0.075 + 0.07} = 4.08 \text{ p.u.}$$

Now,

$$\text{unit (rated) current} = \frac{20\,000}{\sqrt{3} \times 6.6} = 1750 \text{ amp}$$

$$\therefore \qquad I_{R0} = 4.08 \times 1750 = 7140$$

and

$$|I_R| = 3I_{R0} = 21\,420 \text{ amp}$$

(b)   All 3 zero-sequence component currents flow through the earth resistor of 0.2 ohm. Hence the effective additional $Z_0 (= 3 \times 0.2 = 0.6 \text{ ohm})$, $= (0.6 + j0)$ ohm. Now

$$0.6 \text{ ohm} = \frac{0.6 \times 1750 \times \sqrt{3}}{6600} = 0.275 \text{ p.u.}$$

Hence in this case,

$$I_{R0} \text{ (p.u.)} = \frac{1}{0.275 + j0.245}$$

$$|I_{R0}| = \frac{1}{(0.076 + 0.06)^{1/2}} = \frac{1}{0.3685} = 2.71 \text{ p.u.}$$

$$= 2.71 \times 1750 = 4745 \text{ amp}$$

Then

$$|I_R| = 3I_{R0} = 14\,235 \text{ amp}$$

Example 84

Each end of two parallel 3-phase 66 kV feeders has a 3-phase star-connected 100 MW synchronous generator. Each end is fed through a star-star transformer. Positive, negative and zero-sequence reactances, per unit, are $j0.15$, $j0.1$ and $j0.03$ respectively for each generator, and $j0.4$, $j0.4$ and $j0.7$ for each line. The per unit sequence-reactances are each $j0.15$ for the transformer at end A, and $j0.1$ for the transformer at end B. All star-points are solidly earthed except that of generator B which is insulated. Per unit values are based on 100 MVA. Calculate the fault current for a double-line-to-earth fault at the feeder terminals on transformer A.

Solution.   (Ref. 7)

A line-diagram of the system and the sequence-impedance networks can be drawn as in Fig. 84. For the positive and negative sequence currents parallel routes from the generators to the fault occur. But zero-sequence current can flow only from the machine with earthed star-point.

Hence the equivalent sequence-reactances to the fault are,

$$Z_1 = \frac{(0.15 + 0.15)(0.2 + 0.1 + 0.15)}{(0.15 + 0.15) + (0.2 + 0.1 + 0.15)}$$

$$= \frac{0.3 \times 0.45}{0.75} = \frac{0.135}{0.75} = 0.18$$

$$Z_2 = \frac{(0.1 + 0.15)(0.2 + 0.1 + 0.1)}{(0.1 + 0.15) + (0.2 + 0.1 + 0.1)}$$

$$= \frac{0.25 \times 0.4}{0.25 + 0.4} = \frac{0.1}{0.65} = 0.154$$

$$Z_0 = 0.03 + 0.15 = 0.18$$

For a double-line-to-earth fault, (see Example 82),

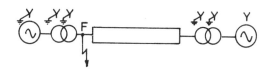

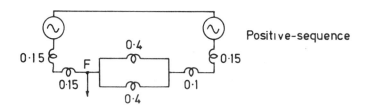

Positive-sequence

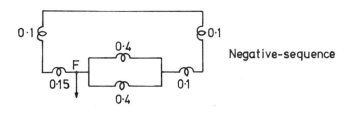

Negative-sequence

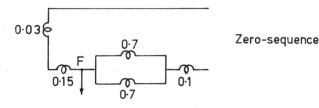

Zero-sequence

Fig. 84

$$I_1 = \frac{1}{Z_1 + [Z_0 Z_2/(Z_0 + Z_2)]} = \frac{1}{j(0.18 + 0.083)}$$

$$= -j3.8 \text{ p.u.}$$

$$I_2 = -I_1 \left(\frac{Z_0}{Z_0 + Z_2} \right) = j3.8 \left(\frac{0.18}{0.18 + 0.154} \right)$$

$$= j2.05$$

$$I_0 = -I_1\left(\frac{Z_2}{Z_0 + Z_2}\right) = j3.8\left(\frac{0.154}{0.334}\right)$$

$$= j1.75$$

(Check: $I_R = I_1 + I_2 + I_0 = 0$.)

$$I_Y = I_{R0} + \lambda^2 I_{R1} + \lambda I_{R2}$$

$$= j1.75 + (-0.5 - j0.866)(-j3.8) + (-0.5 + j0.866)(j2.05)$$

$$= j1.75 + j1.9 - 3.29 - j1.02 - 1.775$$

$$= -5.065 + j2.64$$

$$|I_Y| = |I_B| = [(5.065)^2 + (2.64)^2]^{1/2} = 5.71 \text{ p.u.}$$

Unit (rated) current, at feeder,

$$= \frac{100 \times 10^6}{\sqrt{3} \times 66 \times 10^3} = 875 \text{ amp}$$

∴   Fault current $= 5.71 \times 875 = 4996$ amp

Interpretation of the sequence impedances is assisted by drawing the sequence networks to the fault, as shown in Fig. 84.

Chapter Seven
Power Systems

Example 85

Two 50 Hz power systems designated A and B, have stiffness coefficients of 500 MW/Hz and 750 MW/Hz respectively and are connected by a tie-line. The load on system A increases suddenly by 300 MW. It is required to determine:
  (a) the power transfer across the tie-line, and
  (b) the new frequency of the combined systems.

Solution

Normally the capacity of tie-lines used in large interconnected power systems is much smaller than that of the power systems concerned. Hence power transfers must be carefully monitored so that the capacity of a tie-line is not exceeded. Permissible power flows in tie-lines are decided in advance and are costed. They are computer controlled to certain maximum values.

The change in power for a given change in frequency in a system is known as the stiffness of the system. The stiffness coefficient, $K = \mathrm{d}P/\mathrm{d}f$, may be approximated by a straight line and is a constant depending on the generator governor and load characteristics.

In general, for the system described,

$$\mathrm{d}P = \text{sudden increase of load on system } A$$

Because of tie-line, B supplies extra power $\mathrm{d}P_t$ and so the change in power generated at A is $(\mathrm{d}P - \mathrm{d}P_t)$.

$$\text{Change in frequency at } A = -\frac{(\mathrm{d}P - \mathrm{d}P_t)}{K_A}$$

where $-ve$ sign signifies a fall in frequency, K_A = stiffness coefficient for system A.

The change in frequency at B is the same since A and B are joined electrically; also

$$\text{Frequency change at } B = \frac{\mathrm{d}P_t}{K_B}$$

Assuming a zero power flow in the tie-line initially,

$$\frac{300 - dP_t}{K_A} = \frac{dP_t}{K_B} \quad \text{in MW}$$

$$(300 - dP_t)K_B = (dP_t)K_A$$

$$900 - 3\,dP_t = 2\,dP_t$$

$$5\,dP_t = 900$$

Hence,

power flow, $dP_t = 180\,\text{MW}$ from B to A.

Also,

$$\text{change in } f_B = \frac{180}{750} = 0.24\,\text{Hz}$$

and

$$\text{change in } f_A = \frac{120}{500} = 0.24\,\text{Hz}$$

New frequency of interconnected system

$$= 50 - 0.24 = 49.76\,\text{Hz}$$

Example 86

Three 60 MVA synchronous generators, each having a transient reactance of 0.25 p.u., supply 11.8 kV busbars. The three busbar sections are interconnected by current-limiting reactors in tie-bar fashion as shown in Fig. 86(a). Calculate the value of limiting reactor necessary to limit the fault to 550 MVA in the case of a symmetrical 3-phase short-circuit on a busbar section. Per unit bases are 60 MVA and 11.8 kV.

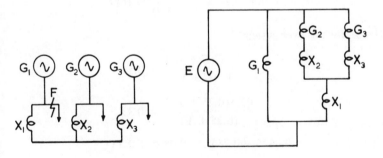

Figs. 86 (a, b)

Solution

The equivalent single-phase network for the system and the given fault condition, can be drawn as in Fig. 86(b).

We are given $G_1 = G_2 = G_3 = 0.25$ p.u.

The fault can occur on any of the busbar sections, so we can say $X_1 = X_2 = X_3 = X$, the current-limiting reactor.

From Fig. 86(b) the equivalent reactance from voltage source to fault = X_e where

$$\frac{1}{X_e} = \frac{1}{G} + \frac{1}{\left(\dfrac{G+X}{2}\right) + X} = \frac{1}{G} + \frac{2}{G + X + 2X}$$

$$= \frac{G + 3X + 2G}{G(G + 3X)} = \frac{3(G + X)}{G(G + 3X)}$$

Hence

$$X_e = \frac{1}{3}\frac{G(G + 3X)}{(G + X)}$$

Now

$$I_{sc} = \frac{E}{X} = \frac{EI_{FL}}{EX_{pu}} = I_{FL}/X_{pu}$$

3-phase Short-circuit

$$VA = \sqrt{3}EI_{sc} = \sqrt{3}EI_{FL}/X_{pu}$$

$$= \frac{\text{Base or Full-Load } VA}{X_{pu}}$$

Permissible S/C VA, (given) $= 550\,\text{MVA} = \dfrac{60}{X_{pu}}$

$\therefore$ Required $X_{pu} = \dfrac{60}{550} = 0.11$

Hence, for the given system,

$$\frac{1}{3}\frac{G(G + 3X)}{(G + X)} = 0.11$$

$$\frac{0.25(0.25 + 3X)}{(0.25 + X)} = 0.33$$

$$0.0625 + 0.75X = 0.0825 + 0.33X$$

$\therefore$ $X = \dfrac{0.02}{0.42} = 0.0476$ p.u.

Now

$$I_{FL} = \frac{60 \times 10^6}{\sqrt{3} \times 11.8 \times 10^3} = 2935\text{ amp}$$

and

$$X(\text{ohm}) = \frac{X_{pu}E_{ph}}{I_{FL}} = \frac{0.0476 \times 11.8 \times 10^3}{2935.2 \times \sqrt{3}}$$

$$= 0.1105 \text{ ohm}$$

The current rating is determined by permissible fault current, viz;

$$\text{Permissible } I_{\text{fault}} = \frac{550 \times 10^6}{\sqrt{3} \times 11.8 \times 10^3}$$

$$= 26\,911 \text{ amp}$$

Example 87

A 132 kV transmission line of impedance $(20 + j53)$ ohm/ph links a constant 11 kV supply to a load of $(60 + j29)$ MVA on 3-phase remote 11 kV busbars. Both the sending end and receiving end of the line has a transformer of nominal 11 kV/132 kV rating equipped with tap changing facilities. It is required to determine the tap settings, expressed in per unit of nominal setting, to maintain the load busbars at 11 kV; and that the product of the settings is unity.

Solution

The tap settings have to compensate for the line volt drop. From the geometry of the voltage phasor diagram, (by approx),

$$IZ \simeq \Delta V = IR \cos \phi + IX \sin \phi$$

Also,

$$(P + jQ) = V(I \cos \phi + jI \sin \phi) = VI^* \quad (\text{Ref. 7, p. 464})$$

Due to the tapping at receiving end,

$$\text{volts at receiving end} = t_R V_2$$

∴

$$\Delta V = \frac{RP + XQ}{t_R V_2} = IZ$$

Hence,

$$t_S V_1 - t_R V_2 = \frac{RP + XQ}{t_R V_2}$$

Now $t_S t_R = 1$ (given),

∴

$$t_S = \frac{1}{V_1}\left[\frac{V_2}{t_S} + \frac{t_S(RP + XQ)}{V_2}\right]$$

$$t_S^2 = \frac{V_2}{V_1} + \left(\frac{RP + XQ}{V_1 V_2}\right) t_S^2$$

$$t_S^2 \left(1 - \frac{RP + XQ}{V_1 V_2}\right) = \frac{V_2}{V_1}$$

For exact compensation, $V_1 = V_2 (= V)$

$$\therefore \qquad t_S^2 = \frac{V^2}{V^2 - (RP + XQ)}$$

Given $V = 132/\sqrt{3}\,\text{kV}; P = 60, Q = 29,$

$$\therefore \qquad t_S^2 = \frac{(132)^2 \times 10^6}{(132)^2 \times 10^6 - 3\left(\dfrac{20 \times 60 \times 10^6 + 53 \times 29 \times 10^6}{3}\right)}$$

$$= \frac{(132)^2}{(132)^2 - (20 \times 60 + 53 \times 29)}$$

$$= \frac{17\,424}{17\,424 - 2737} = 1.186$$

$$\therefore \qquad t_S = 1.09 \quad \text{and} \quad t_R = \frac{1}{1.09} = 0.92$$

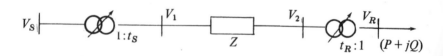

These values are within the normal maximum of ± 20% of tap-changing transformers. In the case of larger tapping requirements, it becomes necessary to inject VAR's to maintain the voltage at the required value, usually from a synchronous compensator.

Example 88

A load of 500 MW at 275 kV and unity power factor is shared by two 3-phase lines. Line A has impedance of $(1 + j6)$ ohm/conductor and line B impedance $(1.6 + j9)$ ohm/conductor. It is required to calculate the power, active and reactive, which should be carried by each line to achieve maximum transmission efficiency. Losses in load-sharing equipment may be ignored.

Solution

A schematic diagram of the system may be drawn;

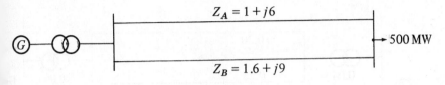

$$Z_A = 1 + j6$$

500 MW

$$Z_B = 1.6 + j9$$

Fig. 88

Let

$$\text{power delivered by line } A = P_A + jQ_A$$
$$\text{power delivered by line } B = P_B + jQ_B$$

For minimal line losses, the currents must be minimal, thus $Q_A = Q_B = 0$.
Hence

$$I_A = P_A/\sqrt{3}\,V \text{ and } I_A \propto P_A \quad \therefore \text{ Power loss in } A \propto P_A^2 \times 1$$
$$I_B = P_B/\sqrt{3}\,V \text{ and } I_B \propto P_B \quad \therefore \text{ Power loss in } B \propto P_B^2 \times 1.6$$

From given data, $P_B = (500 - P_A)$

$$\text{Power loss in } B \propto (500 - P_A)^2 \times 1.6$$
$$\text{Total power loss} \propto P_a^2 + (250\,000 - 1000 P_A + P_A^2)\,1.6$$
$$= 2.6 P_A^2 - 1600 P_A + 400\,000 = P_L$$

This is minimum when $dP_L/dP_A = $ zero, that is

$$5.2 P_A - 1600 = 0$$

Hence,

$$P_A = \frac{1600}{5.2} = 307.6 \text{ MW} \qquad \text{with } Q_A = 0$$

$$P_B = 500 - 307.6 = 192.4 \text{ MW} \quad \text{with } Q_B = 0$$

is the loading for maximum transmission efficiency.

Example 89

Three-phase infinite busbars of voltage 1.0 per unit are supplied from a
generator of excitation emf 1.25 per unit by means of four transmission lines
and transformers connected as represented in the schematic diagram, Fig. 89a.
Per unit values of the various reactances are indicated. It is required to obtain
an expression for the power transmitted to the infinite busbars in terms of
load angle, δ, for the system;

(a) under normal conditions, and

(b) when a solid three-phase earth fault occurs at F, the midpoint of the line of 0.4 p.u. reactance.

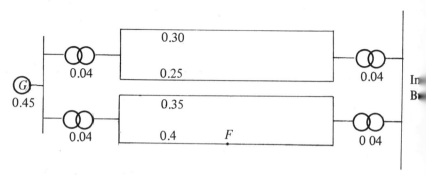

Fig. 89a

Solution

$$\text{The power transmitted} = \frac{VE}{X_s + X_{net}} \sin \delta.$$

We simplify the transmission network to determine X_{net}.

(a) *Normal conditions.*   As the lines are in parallel, the circuit may be redrawn as follows,

$$0.04 + \frac{0.3 \times 0.25}{0.55} + 0.04 \qquad \Sigma = 0.216$$

$$\text{Bus}$$

$$0.04 + \frac{0.35 \times 0.4}{0.75} + 0.04 \qquad \Sigma = 0.267$$

(G)
0.45

Hence

$$\text{total p.u. reactance, } G \text{ to Bus} = 0.45 + 0.119 = 0.569$$

$$\text{Power transmitted} = \frac{1.25 \times 1.0}{0.569} \sin \delta = 2.20 \sin \delta$$

(b) *Fault conditions.*   We redraw the network. Some figures obtained for the healthy part of the system are available from Part (a). The diagram shows reactance values and susceptance values, (in brackets). Eliminate node B by replacing the star AB, CB, and FB by the equivalent delta connection. Remember that for admittances the form of the star-delta transformation formulae is different to that for impedances, viz. Fig. 89b.

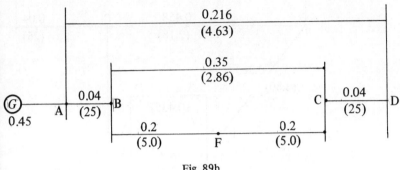

Fig. 89b

In general we have:

$$Z_{12} = \frac{Z_1 Z_3 + Z_2 Z_3 + Z_1 Z_2}{Z_3} = \frac{1}{Y_{12}} = \frac{\dfrac{1}{Y_1 Y_2} + \dfrac{1}{Y_2 Y_3} + \dfrac{1}{Y_1 Y_2}}{\dfrac{1}{Y_3}}$$

Hence

$$Y_{12} = \frac{Y_1 Y_2}{Y_1 + Y_2 + Y_3}$$

(by mult. previous line by $Y_1 Y_2 Y_3$ above and below.)

For the susceptances,

$$B_{AC} = \frac{B_{AB} B_{CB}}{B_{AB} + B_{CB} + B_{FB}} = \frac{(25 \times 2.86)}{(25 + 2.86 + 5)} = (2.18); \quad X_{AC} = 0.458$$

$$B_{FA} = \frac{B_{AB} B_{FB}}{B_{AB} + B_{CB} + B_{FB}} = \frac{(25 \times 5)}{(32.86)} = (3.80); \quad X_{FA} = 0.263$$

$$B_{CF} = \frac{B_{BC} B_{FB}}{B_{AB} + B_{CB} + B_{FB}} = \frac{(2.86 \times 5)}{(32.86)} = (0.435); \quad X_{CF} = 2.30$$

Redrawing the circuit (Fig. 89c);

Branch FC resolves to $X = 0.184;$ $B = (5.44).$

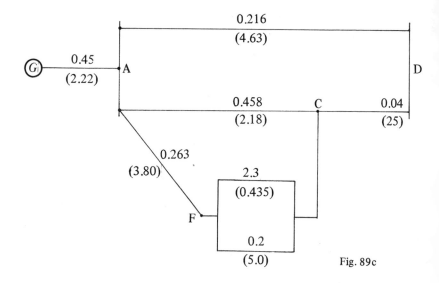

Fig. 89c

We eliminate node C by converting star AC, DC, FC into delta, viz;

$$B_{AD} = \frac{B_{AC}B_{DC}}{B_{AC}+B_{DC}+B_{FC}} = \frac{(2.18 \times 25)}{(2.18 + 25 + 5.44)} = (1.67); \quad X_{AD} = 0.599$$

$$B'_{FA} = \frac{B_{AC}B_{FC}}{B_{AC}+B_{DC}+B_{FC}} = \frac{(2.18 \times 5.44)}{(32.62)} = (0.364); \quad X'_{FA} = 2.75$$

Redrawing the circuit (Fig. 89d);

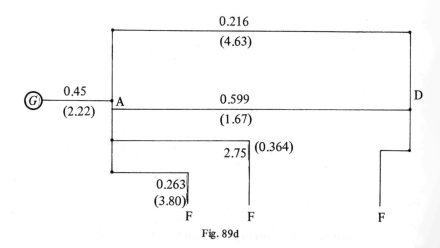

Fig. 89d

Eliminating node A;

$$B_{GD} = \frac{B_{GA}B_{DA}}{B_{GA} + B_{FA} + B_{DA}} = \frac{(2.22 \times 6.30)}{(2.22 + 4.164 + 6.30)}$$

$$= (1.106); \quad X_{GD} = 0.904$$

Then,

$$P_{(b)} = \frac{1.25}{0.904} \sin \delta = 1.38 \sin \delta$$

Example 90

A 3-phase transmission network connects infinite busbars to a generator through a step-up transformer. The generator has excitation emf of 1.2 p.u., and the busbar voltage is 1.0 p.u. The network, with per unit reactance values, (susceptance values bracketed), is described in diagram, Fig. 90. It is required to determine:

(a) the per-unit power delivered to the busbars under normal conditions, in terms of load angle, δ;

(b) the new value of excitation voltage and the load angle when the power delivered to the busbars is $(1.5 + j0.75)$ p.u.

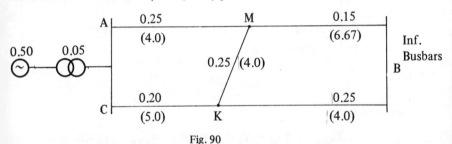

Fig. 90

Solution

Part (a).   The network is simplified by the use of star-delta transformation, in the form for admittances, viz;

$$Y_{12} = \frac{Y_1 Y_2}{Y_1 + Y_2 + Y_3}$$

Working in susceptance values, (bracketed) we transform the star AM, KM, BM, so that M is eliminated.

$$B_{AB} = \frac{B_{AM}B_{BM}}{B_{AM} + B_{BM} + B_{KM}} = \frac{(4 \times 6.67)}{(4 + 4 + 6.67)} = (1.82); \quad X_{AB} = 0.55$$

Also;

$$B_{\text{KA}} = \frac{(4 \times 4)}{(14.67)} = (1.091); \quad X_{\text{KA}} = 0.917$$

$$B_{\text{BK}} = B_{\text{AB}} = (1.82); \quad X_{\text{BK}} = 0.55$$

The network can be redrawn:

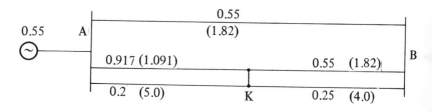

Further simplification gives;

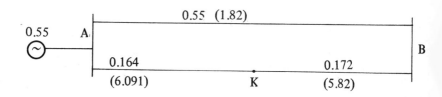

Now we have

$$X_{\text{AKB}} = X_{\text{AK}} + X_{\text{KB}} = 0.336; \quad B_{\text{AKB}} = (2.97)$$

$$\text{Parallel line } B_{\text{AB}} = (1.82)$$

Then,

$$\text{total } B_{\text{AB}} = (4.79); \quad X_{\text{AB}} = 0.2085 = X_{\text{net}}$$

$$\text{Power to busbars} = \frac{VE}{X_{\text{gen}} + X_{\text{net}}} \sin \delta = 1.58 \sin \delta$$

Part (b).

$$\text{New power to bus} = P + jQ = 1.5 + j0.75$$

$$= VI (\cos \phi + j \sin \phi)$$

From the geometry of the phasor diagram;

$$E^2 = (V + IR \cos \phi + IX \sin \phi)^2 + (IX \cos \phi - IR \sin \phi)^2$$

$$= \left(V + \frac{RP}{V} + \frac{XQ}{V}\right)^2 + \left(\frac{XP}{V} - \frac{RQ}{V}\right)^2$$

If R is negligible;

$$E^2 = \left(V + \frac{XQ}{V}\right)^2 + \left(\frac{XP}{V}\right)^2$$

Substituting known values;

$$E^2 = \left(1 + \frac{0.759 \times 0.75}{1}\right)^2 + \left(\frac{0.759 \times 1.5}{1}\right)^2$$

$$= 2.45 + 1.3 = 2.75$$

Hence $E = 1.66$ p.u. Also,

$$\sin \delta = \frac{XP}{VE} = \frac{1.139}{1.66} = 0.685$$

$$\delta = 43.2°$$

Example 91

Two substations, B and C, are separately supplied from a generating station A of busbar voltage $V_A = 1.2$ per unit, through feeders of reactances 0.4 p.u. and 0.75 p.u. respectively. The substations are joined by an interconnector of reactance 0.5 p.u. Substation B has an external load current of $(0.5 - j0.35)$ p.u., and substation C a load current of $(0.6 - j0.2)$ p.u., both referred to V_A. It is required to determine the busbar voltage and active and reactive power outputs of each station.

Solution

The network may be drawn schematically (Fig. 91).

$$\text{Total current from } A = I_{AB} + I_{AC} = I_B + I_C$$

$$= 1.1 - j0.55 \qquad (1)$$

By Kirchhoff's current Law,

$$I_{AC} + I_{BC} = I_C = 0.6 - j0.2 \qquad (2)$$

$$I_{AB} - I_{BC} = I_B = 0.5 - j0.35 \qquad (3)$$

By Kirchhoff's voltage Law,

$$0.4I_{AB} + 0.5I_{BC} - 0.75I_{AC} = 0 \qquad (4)$$

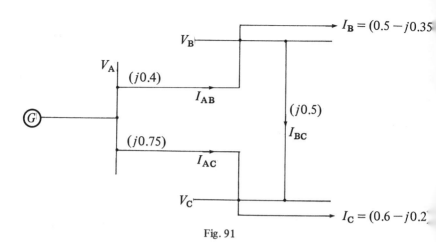

Fig. 91

$(4) \times 2$	$0.8I_{AB} + I_{BC} - 1.5I_{AC} = 0$
From (3)	$I_{AB} - I_{BC} \qquad = 0.5 - j0.35$
Adding	$1.8I_{AB} - 1.5I_{AC} = 0.5 - j0.35$
$(1) \times 1.5$	$1.5I_{AB} + 1.5I_{AC} = 1.65 - j0.825$

Adding, $3.3I_{AB} = 2.15 - j1.175$

Whence $I_{AB} = 0.652 - j0.356$

From (3) $I_{BC} = I_{AB} - (0.5 - j0.35) = 0.152 - j0.006$

From (2) $I_{AC} = (0.6 - j0.2) - I_{BC} = 0.448 - j0.194$

Now
$$V_B = V_A - I_{AB}(j0.4) = 1.2 - (0.652 - j0.356)(j0.4)$$
$$= 1.2 - (0.142 + j0.261) = (1.058 - j0.261) \text{ p.u.}$$
$$V_C = V_A - I_{AC}(j0.75) = 1.2 - (0.448 - j0.194)(j0.75)$$
$$= (1.054 - j0.338) \text{ p.u.}$$

Power from B $= S_B = V_B I_B^*$

where I_B^* is the conjugate of I_B

$$= (1.058 - j0.261)(0.5 + j0.35)$$
$$= (0.62 + j0.24) \text{ p.u.}$$

Power from C $= S_C = V_C I_C^*$

$$= (1.054 - j0.338)(0.6 + j0.2)$$

$$= (0.70 + j0.008)$$

Power from A $= S_A = V_A I_A^* = (1.2)(1.1 + j0.55)$

$$= (1.32 + j0.66)$$

N.B. Note that $S_B + S_C = 1.32 + j0.248$. The extra reactive power supplied by A is required by the reactances in the network, viz;

$I_{AB} = (0.652 - j0.356)$ p.u. $|I_{AB}|^2 X_{AB} = 0.5517 \times 0.4 = 0.221$

$I_{AC} = (0.448 - j0.194)$ p.u. $|I_{AC}|^2 X_{AC} = 0.240 \times 0.75 = 0.18$

$I_{BC} = (0.152 - j0.006)$ p.u. $|I_{BC}|^2 X_{BC} = 0.0231 \times 0.5 = 0.0115$

Then reactive power for the network $= (0.221 + 0.18 + 0.0115)$ or $S_{net} = j0.4125$ whence

$$S_A = S_B + S_C + S_{net}$$

Example 92

A 3-phase 50 Hz overhead transmission line 200 km long has the following primary constants: $R = 0.06$ ohm per conductor per km, $L = 1.20$ millihenry per conductor per km, $C = 0.014$ microfarad per conductor per km to neutral, G is negligible.

It is required to know the sending end voltage, current and power factor, if the load at the receiving end is 180 MVA at 250 kV and 0.9 power factor lagging.

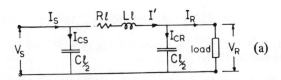

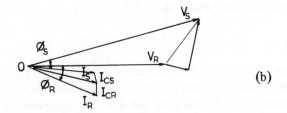

Fig. 92

Solution

The nominal-π solution is acceptable when $l < 300$ km. The per phase circuit and notation is given in Fig. 92(a)

$$|I_R| = \frac{180 \times 10^6}{\sqrt{3} \times 250 \times 10^3} = 416 \text{ ampere}$$

$$I_R = 416(\cos \phi - j \sin \phi) = 416(0.9 - j0.436)$$

$$= 374 - j181 \quad \text{assuming } V_R \text{ is the reference phasor}$$

$$V_R = \frac{250 \times 10^3}{\sqrt{3}} = 144.3 \text{ kV/phase}$$

$$I_{CR} = j\omega C \frac{l}{2} V_R = j(314)\left(\frac{0.014 \times 10^{-6} \times 200}{2}\right)(144.3 \times 10^3)$$

$$= j63.5 \text{ ampere}$$

$$I' = I_R + I_{CR} = (374 - j181) + (+j63.5) = (374 - j117.5)$$

$$V_S = V_R + I'Zl = 144.3 \times 10^3 + (374 - j117.5)\left(0.06 + j\frac{314 \times 1.2}{10^3}\right) \times 200$$

$$= (158 + j26.8) \times 10^3 = 160 \times 10^3 \underline{/9°38'}$$

Hence

Line value (magnitude) of $V_S = 160 \text{ kV} \times \sqrt{3} = 277 \text{ kV}.$

$$I_S = I' + I_{CS} = (374 - j118)$$

$$+ j(314)\left(\frac{0.014 \times 10^{-6} \times 200}{2}\right)(158 + j26.8) \times 10^3$$

$$= 362 - j48.5 = 365 \underline{/-7°38'}$$

Thus, V_S leads V_R by $9°38'$ and I_S lags V_R by $7°38'$ and current lags voltage at sending end by $17°16'$.

Sending end power factor $= \cos 17°16' = 0.956$ lagging

The phasor diagram is shown in Fig. 92(b).

Example 93

A 3-phase 50 Hz 275 kV overhead transmission line of length 200 km has the following primary constants per conductor per kilometre; $R = 0.03$ ohm, $L = 1.06$ millihenry, G is negligible and $C = 0.01$ microfarad to neutral. It is required to know the voltage at the receiving-end if the load of 250 MVA at

0.85 power factor lagging, is thrown off, the sending-end voltage being maintained constant.

Solution

For this distance a nominal-π circuit is sufficiently accurate, shown schematically in Fig. 93;

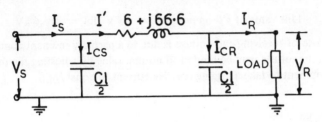

Fig. 93

The necessary constants are;

$$Rl = 0.03 \times 200 = 6 \text{ ohm}$$

$$\omega Ll = 314 \times 1.06 \times 10^{-3} \times 200 = 66.6 \text{ ohm}$$

$$\omega Cl = 314 \times 0.01 \times 10^{-6} \times 200 = 0.628 \times 10^{-3}$$

On load;

$$V_R = \frac{275 \times 10^3}{\sqrt{3}} = 159 \times 10^3 \text{ volt/phase}$$

$$I_R = \frac{250 \times 10^6}{\sqrt{3} \times 275 \times 10^3} \underline{/-31°47'} = 525 \underline{/-31°47'}$$

$$= 446 - j277 \text{ ampere}$$

$$I_{CR} = j159 \times 10^3 \times \frac{0.628 \times 10^{-3}}{2} = j50 \text{ ampere}$$

$$I' = I_R + I_{CR} = 446 - j277 + j50 = 446 - j227 \text{ ampere}$$

$$V_S = V_R + I'Zl = 159 \times 10^3 + (446 - j227)(6 + j66.6)$$

$$= 176.8 \times 10^3 + j28.3 \times 10^3 = 179 \times 10^3 \underline{/9°6'} \text{ volt}$$

Conditions on no load;

$$I_R = 0 \quad \text{and } I' \text{ becomes} \quad I'' = \frac{V_S}{(R + j\omega L)l + 2(1/j\omega Cl)}$$

Thus

$$I'' = \frac{179 \times 10^3}{(6 + j66.6) + (10^3/j0.314)} = \frac{179 \times 10^3}{6 - j3118} \hat{=} \frac{179 \times 10^3}{-j3118}$$

$$= +j57.4 \text{ amp}$$

New receiving-end voltage

$$= V_S - I''Zl = 179 \times 10^3 - j57.4(6 + j66.6)$$

$$= 179 \times 10^3 (-j344.4 + 3822.8 = 182.8 \times 10^3 - j344.4)$$

$$\approx 182.8 \times 10^3 \approx 183 \text{ kV}$$

Line value of V_R on no load $= \sqrt{3} \times 183 = 316.6 \text{ kV}$

The rise of receiving-end voltage is due to a partially resonant condition in the line; the voltage may be limited to normal value by adjusting the receiving-end equipment to take a lagging reactive current to equal I_{CR}.

Example 94

A 3-phase 380 kV 50 Hz overhead transmission line 80 kilometres long delivers a unity power factor load of four times the magnitude (in MVA) of the natural impedance load. The primary constants of the line per kilometre per conductor are; $R = 0.03$ ohm, $L = 1.10 \text{ mH}$, G is negligible and $C = 0.01 \, \mu\text{F}$ to neutral. It is required to determine the sending-end voltage and its phase shift relative to the receiving-end voltage.

Solution

Terminal conditions of a line may be represented in terms of 4-terminal network constants, viz;

$$V_S = AV_R + BI_R$$

$$I_S = CV_R + DI_R$$

Where the conditions at the load are known, the general line equations are;

$$V_S = V_R \cosh Pl + I_R Z_0 \sinh Pl$$

$$I_S = \frac{V_R}{Z_0} \sinh Pl + I_R \cosh Pl$$

where

$$Z_0 = \text{natural impedance} = \sqrt{\frac{Z}{Y}}$$

and

$$P = \text{propagation constant} = (\alpha + j\beta) \quad \text{and} \quad Pl = \sqrt{ZY}$$

In this case, to determine V_S we require,

$$A = \cosh Pl = \cosh \sqrt{ZY}$$

$$B = Z_0 \sinh Pl = \sqrt{\frac{Z}{Y}} \sinh \sqrt{ZY}$$

From the given data,

$$Z = l(R + j\omega L) = 80(0.03 + j314.2 \times 1.1 \times 10^{-3})$$

$$= 80(0.03 + j0.346) = (24.0 + j27.7)$$

or,

$$= 80(0.347\underline{/85°3'}) = 27.8\underline{/85°3'}$$

$$Y = l(G + j\omega C) = 80(0 + j314.2 \times 0.01 \times 10^{-6})$$

$$= 80(3.142 \times 10^{-6}\underline{/90°}) = 251.4 \times 10^{-6}\underline{/90°}$$

$$ZY = 27.8\underline{/85°3'} \times 251.4 \times 10^{-6}\underline{/90°} = 6.99 \times 10^{-3}\underline{/175°3'}$$

$$Z_0 = \sqrt{\frac{Z}{Y}} = \left(\frac{27.8}{251.4 \times 10^{-6}}\underline{/85°3' - 90°}\right)^{1/2} = 333\underline{/-2°28'}$$

Natural impedance loading $= \dfrac{V_R^2}{Z_0}$ and in MVA $= \dfrac{(380)^2}{333} = 433.7$

Four times natural impedance loading $= 1735$ MVA

$$\text{Corresponding } I_R = \frac{1735}{\sqrt{3} \times 380} = 2.636\,\text{kA} = 2636\underline{/0°}\ \text{amp}$$

Hyperbolic functions can be expressed;

$$\sinh x = x + \frac{x^3}{\underline{|3}} + \frac{x^5}{\underline{|5}} + \ldots \quad \text{etc}$$

$$\cosh x = 1 + \frac{x^2}{\underline{|2}} + \frac{x^4}{\underline{|4}} + \ldots \quad \text{etc}$$

Approximations are admissible by taking a few terms, say the first two terms for a short line. Then

$$A = \cosh Pl = \cosh \sqrt{ZY} \simeq \left(1 + \frac{ZY}{2}\right)$$

$$= \left(1 + \frac{6.99 \times 10^{-3}}{2}\underline{/175°3'}\right) = 1 + \left(-\frac{3.481}{10^3} + j\frac{0.3017}{10^3}\right)$$

$$= 0.9965 + j0.0003$$

$$AV_R = \frac{380}{\sqrt{3}}(0.9965 + j0.0003) = (218.6 + j0.07)\,\text{kV}$$

$$B = Z_0 \sinh Pl = \sqrt{\frac{Z}{Y}} \sinh \sqrt{ZY} \simeq Z\left(1 + \frac{ZY}{6}\right)$$

$$BI_R = 2.636(27.8\underline{/85°3'})\left[1 + \left(-\frac{1.16}{10^3} + j\frac{0.1006}{10^3}\right)\right]$$

$$= 2.636(2.4 + j27.7)(0.999) = (6.322 + j73.0)\,\text{kV}$$

$$\therefore \qquad V_S = AV_R + BI_R = (218.6 + j0.07) + (6.322 + j73.0)$$

$$= 224.9 + j73.1 = 239.3\underline{/17°47'}$$

Hence, line value of $V_S = \sqrt{3} \times 239.3 = 414\,\text{kV}$ leading V_R by $17°47'$.

N.B. *Short line approx. as a check*: (corresponds to one term only in series).

$$V_S \simeq V_R + I_R Z$$

$$= 219 + 2.636(2.4 + j27.7)$$

$$= 219 + 6.33 + j73.03 = 225.3 + j73.03$$

$$= 236.9\underline{/17°57'}\,\text{kV}$$

Line value of $V_S = \sqrt{3} \times 236.9 = 410.2\,\text{kV}$ leading $17°57'$ on V_R.

Example 95

The parameters of a 275 kV 3-phase transmission line are given as follows; reactance 0.51 ohm/mile/phase and susceptance 5.82×10^{-6} ohm/mile/phase. It is required to determine the length of line for which the input current at rated voltage with the distant end short-circuited is equal to the input current with the distant end open-circuited.

Solution.   (Ref. 7, p. 78; Ref. 16, p. 107)

Long line theory gives,

$$V_s = V_r \cosh Pl + I_r Z_0 \sinh Pl$$

$$I_s = I_r \cosh Pl + \frac{V_r}{Z_0} \sinh Pl$$

On short circuit, $V_r = 0$ and hence,

$$Z_{sc} = \frac{V_s}{I_s} = \frac{I_r Z_0 \sinh Pl}{I_r \cosh Pl} = Z_0 \tanh Pl$$

On open circuit, $I_r = 0$ and hence,

$$Z_{oc} = \frac{V_s}{I_s} = \frac{V_r \cosh Pl}{\dfrac{V_r}{Z_0} \sinh Pl} = Z_0 \coth Pl$$

Thus,

$$Z_{sc} Z_{oc} = Z_0^2$$

Now,

$$\tanh Pl = \frac{\sinh Pl}{\cosh Pl} = \frac{1}{\coth Pl} \quad \text{and} \quad P = \alpha + j\beta$$

Also,

$$\sinh Pl = \sinh \alpha l \cos \beta l + j \cosh \alpha l \sin \beta l$$

$$= j \sin \beta l \quad \text{when} \quad \alpha = 0$$

$$\cosh Pl = \cosh \alpha l \cos \beta l + j \sinh \alpha l \sin \beta l$$

$$= \cos \beta l \quad \text{when} \quad \alpha = 0$$

$$\therefore \qquad Z_{sc} = Z_0 j \tan \beta l$$

Note

$$Z_0 = \sqrt{\left(\frac{R + jX}{G + jB}\right)} = \sqrt{\left(\frac{X}{B}\right)}$$

which is real, when R and $G = 0$ and Z_{sc} is imaginary.

But where $I_{sc} = I_{oc} = I_0$, the magnitudes of Z_0 and Z_{sc} are equal. The required condition is, $\tan \beta l = 1.0$

$$\therefore \qquad \beta l = 0.79 \text{ rad}$$

For the given data,

$$P = \sqrt{[(R + jX)(G + jB)]} = \alpha + j\beta$$

$$= j\sqrt{(BX)} = j\beta \quad \text{for no resistance, } (R \text{ and } G = 0)$$

$$\therefore \qquad \beta = \sqrt{(0.51 \times 5.82 \times 10^{-6})}$$

$$= \sqrt{(2.968 \times 10^{-6})} = 1.723 \times 10^{-3}$$

Hence

$$l = \frac{0.79 \times 10^3}{1.723} = 458.5 \text{ miles} = (458.5 \times 1.609)$$

$$= 737.73 \text{ km}$$

[N.B.   Initial conversion of the non-SI unit, the *mile*, is not essential to the method of solution in this case].

Chapter Eight
Rectifiers and Inverters

Example 96

A single-phase transformer with centre-tapped secondary winding, supplies a
full-wave rectifier. A pure resistance load on the rectifier takes a mean current
of 12 amp. Calculate the necessary cross-sectional area of the conductor in
the transformer secondary winding, assuming a current density of 250 A/cm².

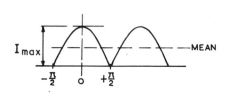
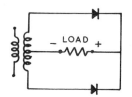

Fig. 96

Solution

Referring to Fig. 96

$$\text{Mean current in load} = \frac{1}{\pi} \int_{-\pi/2}^{+\pi/2} I_{\text{max}} \cos \omega t \, d\omega t$$

$$= \frac{I_{\text{max}}}{\pi} [\sin \omega t]_{-\pi/2}^{+\pi/2}$$

$$= \frac{I_{\text{max}}}{\pi} \times 2 = \frac{2}{\pi} I_{\text{max}} = I_{\text{dc}}$$

$$(\text{r.m.s. value})^2 = \text{mean of } i^2$$

$$= \frac{1}{2\pi} \int_{-\pi/2}^{+\pi/2} I_{\text{max}}^2 \cos^2 \omega t \, d\omega t$$

$$= \frac{I_{\text{max}}^2}{2\pi} \int_{-\pi/2}^{+\pi/2} (\tfrac{1}{2} + \tfrac{1}{2} \cos 2\omega t) \, d\omega t$$

$$= \frac{I_{max}^2}{2\pi} \left[\frac{\omega t}{2} + \frac{1}{4} \sin 2\omega t \right]_{-\pi/2}^{+\pi/2}$$

$$= \frac{I_{max}^2}{2\pi} \left[\frac{\pi}{2} \right] = \frac{I_{max}^2}{4}$$

Hence,

$$\text{r.m.s. value} = \frac{I_{max}}{2} = 0.5 \left(\frac{\pi}{2} I_{dc} \right)$$

$$= \frac{\pi}{4} \times 12 = 9.4 \text{ amp}$$

$\therefore$ Cross-sectional area of conductor $= \dfrac{9.4}{250} = 0.038 \text{ cm}^2$

N.B. Each half of the secondary winding carries current for only half the time, so we must integrate i^2 over half a cycle but average over a whole cycle, to determine the r.m.s. value per winding.

Example 97

A single-phase bridge rectifier is supplied from 240 V, 50 Hz a.c. mains via a 240/325 V transformer. The rectifier supplies 0.6 A to a pure resistance load of 615 ohm. A capacitor input filter gives a specified maximum ripple of 5% of the d.c. voltage. The transformer winding resistances are given, $R_1 = 5.9$ ohm, $R_2 = 22.0$ ohm. It is required to estimate:

(a) the minimum value of input capacitor,

(b) the d.c. output voltage, and

(c) the rectifier ratings, viz; switch-on surge current, I_s, recurrent peak current, I_p, and peak inverse voltage, (PIV).

Solution

The assumption of zero source resistance can lead to serious errors in the design of power supply circuits which use rectifiers. It would not be thought acceptable in this case. The result can be that limitations of peak current and power ratings of the rectifier elements are exceeded. Indeed additional source resistance may require to be added to protect a given diode and the input capacitor against excessive currents.

A design involves a number of inter-related parameters and several solutions are possible. Choice of the most acceptable solution is dictated by the ratings of available components. The nature of the basic mathematics involved is demonstrated in a simplified case, (see Example 98). The iterative process implied is assisted by the use of generalized operation characteristics.

In the present problem significant circuit constants are defined by (i) the ratio $R_{\text{source}}/R_{\text{load}}$ (or R_s/R_L), (ii) $\omega C R_L$, which is related to power factor of the filter circuit. These have been related to voltage and current circumstances in generalized characteristic curves by O.H. Schade, (Ref. Paper 5).

The figure numbers given below relate to this reference.

Numerical part.   Assuming forward resistance/diode = 2 ohm,

$$R_s = \text{total transformer resistance referred to secondary}$$
$$+ (2 \times \text{diode forward resistance})$$

$$= 22 + \left[5.9 \times \left(\frac{325}{240} \right)^2 \right] + 4$$

$$= 36.9 \text{ ohm}$$

Then

$$\frac{R_s}{R_L} = \frac{36.9}{615} = 0.06 \quad \text{or} \quad 6\%$$

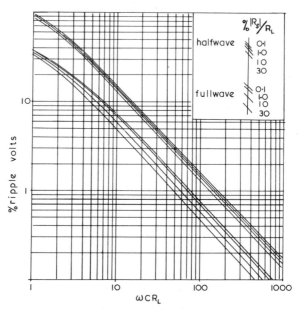

Fig. 97(a)

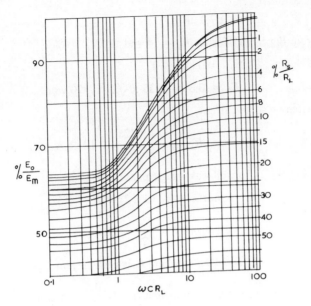

Fig. 97(b)

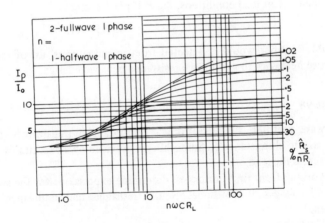

Fig. 97(c)

(a) From Fig. 97(a), for 5% ripple and $R_s/R_L = 6\%$,

$$\omega C R_L = 13$$

$\therefore$
$$C = \frac{13}{314 \times 615} = 67.3 \times 10^{-6} \text{ farad}$$

$$= 67.3 \, \mu F$$

(b) From Fig. 97(b), for $\omega CR_L = 13$ and $R_s/R_L = 6\%$

$$E_0/E_m = 0.805$$

∴

$$E_0 = 0.805 \times 325 \times \sqrt{2} = 370 \text{ volt}$$

(c) Switch-on surge current,

$$I_s = E_m/R_s = \frac{\sqrt{2} \times 325}{36.9} = 12.45 \text{ A}$$

From Fig. 97(c), for full-wave single-phase, $n = 2$,

and taking

$$n\omega CR_L = 13 \times 2 = 26$$

$$\hat{R}_s/nR_L = \frac{6\%}{2} = 3\%$$

$$I_p/I_0 = 7.2 \quad \text{where } I_p \text{ is peak current}$$

$$\text{Now since av. current/rectifier} = \frac{0.6}{2} = 0.3 \text{ A}$$

∴

$$\text{Recurrent peak}, I_p = 0.3 \times 7.2 = 2.16 \text{ A}$$

Under open circuit load conditions, the *PIV* per rectifier

$$= E_m = \sqrt{2} \times 325 = 459.55 \text{ volt}$$

A suitable rectifier would be selected from manufacturers' list of ratings. It may prove necessary to add source resistance in a given design.

Example 98

A full-wave rectifier, supplied from a centre-tapped transformer, supplies current to a load resistance R. Smoothing is provided by a capacitance C, connected across the load.

(a) Working from first principles, determine expressions for the switching times and voltages of the diodes. Source resistance and inductance may be neglected.

(b) Given the condition, $R = 1/\omega C$, determine the voltages and the points in a cycle when switching of the diodes occurs.

Solution

Taking voltage peak as the origin, $t = 0$, (point P, Fig. 98(b)) transformer voltage across diode 1,

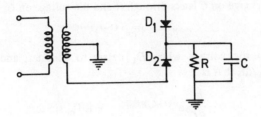

Fig. 98(a)

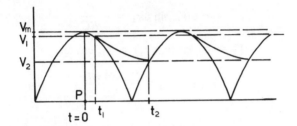

Fig. 98(b)

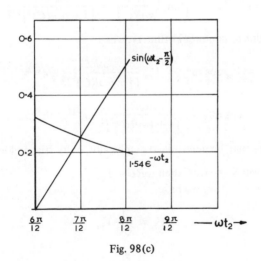

Fig. 98(c)

$$v_T = V_m \cos \omega t$$

The capacitor becomes charged during the rising part of the positive voltage wave. As soon as this voltage becomes less than the voltage on C, diode 1 becomes reverse biassed and is cut off, at t_1.

Then the charge on C leaks through R and the voltage on C,

$$v_c = V_1 e^{-(t-t_1)/RC}$$

where V_1 is the voltage when D_1 ceases to conduct, and occurs when $dv_c/dt = dv_T/dt$, that is

$$-\frac{V_1}{RC} e^{-(t-t_1)/RC} = -\omega V_m \sin \omega t$$

This occurs when $t = t_1$

$\therefore$
$$-\omega V_m \sin \omega t_1 = -\frac{V_1}{RC}$$

Also,

$$V_1 = v_T \text{ (at time } t_1) = V_m \cos \omega t_1$$

Then

$$\omega V_m \sin \omega t_1 = \frac{V_m \cos \omega t_1}{RC}$$

$\therefore$
$$\tan \omega t_1 = \frac{1}{\omega RC}$$

Also

$$V_1 = V_m \cos\left(\tan^{-1} \frac{1}{\omega RC}\right) = \frac{V_m \omega RC}{[1+(\omega RC)^2]^{1/2}}$$

Diode D_2 begins to conduct at time t_2, when

$$V_2 = V_m \cos \omega t_2 = V_m \frac{\omega RC}{[1+(\omega RC)^2]^{1/2}} e^{-(t_2-t_1)/RC}$$

and

$$\cos \omega t_2 = \frac{\omega RC}{[1+(\omega RC)^2]^{1/2}} e^{-(t_2-t_1)/RC}$$

The value of t_2 may be determined graphically, or by trial and error.

Part (b).   Given $R = 1/\omega C$ then $\omega RC = 1$.
   By substitution above we have,

$$V_1 = \frac{1}{\sqrt{2}} V_m$$

and

$$\omega t_1 = \frac{\pi}{4}$$

Also, for V_2, noting the waveform diagram, we have,

$$-\cos \omega t_2 = \frac{1}{\sqrt{2}} e^{(-\omega t_2 + \omega t_1)}$$

$$\sin\left(\omega t_2 - \frac{\pi}{2}\right) = (0.707)(\epsilon^{\pi/4})(\epsilon^{-\omega t_2})$$

$$= 1.54\,\epsilon^{-\omega t_2}$$

Plotting both sides of the equation over the likely range, $6\pi/12$ to $8\pi/12$ we obtain an intercept at $\omega t_2 = 7\pi/12$ (Fig. 98(c)).

Then we have,
$$V_2 = -V_m \cos \omega t_2 = -V_m(-0.25)$$

$$= 0.25\,V_m$$

Example 99

Determine an expression for the mean d.c. output voltage of an N-phase rectifier. Calculate the kVA loading of a star-connected transformer to supply a 3-phase rectifier having a d.c. output of 10 kW at 200 volt. Allow 10% volt drop in the rectifier and assume constant output current and half-wave rectification.

Solution

First part. With polyphase operation, conduction occurs between the cathode and the anode of highest potential. Thus each anode operates over a period $2\pi/N$. Taking the peak value as origin, a.c. voltage/phase $e = E_m \cos \theta$.

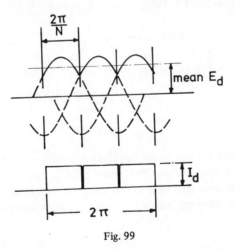

Fig. 99

The mean value of the d.c. voltage is obtained by integrating the voltage waveform over the period $2\pi/N$, thus, (Fig. 99)

$$E_d = \frac{\int\limits_{-\pi/N}^{\pi/N} e\, d\theta}{2\pi/N} = \frac{\int\limits_{-\pi/N}^{\pi/N} E_m \cos\theta\, d\theta}{2\pi/N}$$

$$= \frac{[E_m \sin\theta]_{-\pi/N}^{+\pi/N}}{2\pi/N} = \frac{N}{\pi} E_m \sin\frac{\pi}{N}$$

This value includes the volt drop in the rectifier. For *3-phase bridge*, $N = 6$ forward-going peaks and E_m becomes max E_L (see Fig. 104).

Numerical part.   Mean value of d.c. volts, including volt drop = 220 volt.

$$\text{R.M.S. a.c. phase volts } E = \frac{(\pi/N)E_d}{\sqrt{2}\sin(\pi/N)}$$

$$= \frac{(\pi/3)\, 220}{\sqrt{2}\sin(\pi/3)} = \frac{\pi \times 220 \times 2}{3 \times \sqrt{2} \times \sqrt{3}} = 188.1 \text{ volt}$$

$$\text{D.C. load current } = 10\,000/200 = 50 \text{ amp}$$

Each phase conducts for $2\pi/N$ of each cycle, Fig. 99. Then mean d.c./phase = I_d/N and r.m.s. current/phase (approx.),

$$= \sqrt{\frac{I_d^2}{N}} = I_d/\sqrt{N}$$

(an approximation. See Ex. 100)

$$\therefore \qquad \text{R.M.S. phase current } = \frac{50}{\sqrt{3}} = 28.87 \text{ amp}$$

$$\therefore \qquad \text{3-phase rating of a.c. supply } = 3 \times 188.1 \times 28.87 \times 10^{-3}$$

$$= 16.29 \text{ kVA}$$

Example 100

Derive expressions for the mean and the r.m.s. values of the output current per anode of an N-phase rectifier under natural commutation conditions. Hence show that the magnitude of the output current may be assumed constant at the mean value per anode if the number of phases exceeds 3.

Solution

Each anode current will have a waveform as shown in Fig. 100. Then mean anode current,

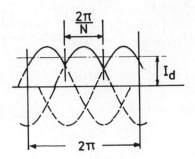

Fig. 100

$$I_d = \frac{1}{2\pi/N} \int_{-\pi/N}^{+\pi/N} I_m \cos\theta \, d\theta$$

$$= \frac{N}{2\pi} I_m [\sin\theta]_{-\pi/N}^{+\pi/N} = \frac{N}{\pi} I_m \sin\frac{\pi}{N}$$

The r.m.s. value of current/anode involves integrating i^2 between limits $-\pi/N$ and $+\pi/N$, and taking the mean over a cycle, thus,

$$I_{\text{rms}} = \left[\frac{1}{2\pi} \int_{-\pi/N}^{+\pi/N} I_m^2 \cos^2\theta \, d\theta\right]^{1/2}$$

$$= \left[\frac{I_m^2}{2\pi} \int_{-\pi/N}^{+\pi/N} (\tfrac{1}{2} + \tfrac{1}{2}\cos 2\theta) \, d\theta\right]^{1/2}$$

$$= \left\{\frac{I_m^2}{2\pi}\left[\frac{\theta}{2} + \frac{\sin 2\theta}{4}\right]_{-\pi/N}^{+\pi/N}\right\}^{1/2}$$

$$= \left\{\frac{I_m^2}{2\pi}\left[\frac{\pi}{2N} + \frac{1}{4}\sin\frac{2\pi}{N} + \frac{\pi}{2N} + \frac{1}{4}\sin\frac{2\pi}{N}\right]\right\}^{1/2}$$

$$= I_m\left[\frac{1}{2N} + \frac{1}{4\pi}\sin\frac{2\pi}{N}\right]^{1/2}$$

With the approximation of a constant output current equal to the mean current, we have,

$$i^2 = I_d^2$$

and the approximate r.m.s. value is then,

$$= \left[\frac{1}{2\pi} \int_{-\pi/N}^{+\pi/N} I_d^2 \, d\theta \right]^{1/2} = I_d \left\{ \frac{1}{2\pi} [\theta]_{-\pi/N}^{+\pi/N} \right\}^{1/2}$$

$$= I_d \left\{ \frac{1}{2\pi} \frac{2\pi}{N} \right\}^{1/2} = I_d/(N)^{1/2}$$

Substituting for I_d, this may be written,

$$= \left(\frac{I_m}{\pi} \sin \frac{\pi}{N} \right) N^{1/2}$$

Now a correction factor K, may be defined,

$$K = \frac{\text{true r.m.s. value}}{\text{approx. r.m.s. value}}$$

$$= \frac{\pi}{N^{1/2} \sin \pi/N} \left[\frac{1}{2N} + \frac{1}{4\pi} \sin \frac{2\pi}{N} \right]^{1/2}$$

For $N = 3$, $K = 1.016$, and for $N > 3$, $K \to 1.0$. Hence the approximation is admissible. Note that $N = 6$ for 3 phase bridge, (full-wave).

Example 101

Derive from first principles expressions for the mean output voltage of an N-phase rectifier, allowing for:

(a) overlap, and

(b) grid control. Hence calculate the mean output voltage of a 3-phase rectifier (i) when the overlap angle is $20°$, (ii) when grid control retards commutation by $20°$. The input voltage is 300 V/phase and the rectifier volt drop may be neglected. (Assume half-wave rectification).

Solution

Part (a).   Due to inductance in the anode circuits, anode current in anode 1 takes a finite time to decay during the time anode 2 current is rising. Hence there is a short time, termed 'overlap', during the commutation period when two anodes are conducting simultaneously. Allowing for the overlap period, the output voltage will be as shown in Fig. 101(a). The mean output voltage is obtained by integrating over the period $2\pi/N$, and is determined as follows;

Taking P as origin, (Fig. 101(a))

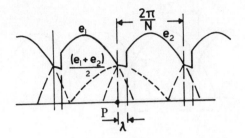

Fig. 101(a)

$$V_d = \frac{1}{2\pi/N}\left[\int_0^\lambda \frac{e_1 + e_2}{2}\,d\theta + \int_\lambda^{2\pi/N} e_2\,d\theta\right]$$

where $e_1 = E_m \cos(\theta + \pi/N)$ and $e_2 = E_m \cos(\theta - \pi/N)$ and $\theta = \omega t$.

$$\therefore V_d = \frac{NE_m}{2\pi}\left[\tfrac{1}{2}\int_0^\lambda \{\cos(\theta+\pi/N) + \cos(\theta-\pi/N)\}\,d\theta + \int_\lambda^{2\pi/N}\cos(\theta-\pi/N)\,d\theta\right]$$

$$= \frac{NE_m}{2\pi}\left\{\tfrac{1}{2}\left[\sin\left(\theta+\frac{\pi}{N}\right) + \sin\left(\theta-\frac{\pi}{N}\right)\right]_0^\lambda + \left[\sin\left(\theta-\frac{\pi}{N}\right)\right]_\lambda^{2\pi/N}\right\}$$

$$= \frac{NE_m}{2\pi}\left\{\tfrac{1}{2}\left[\sin\left(\lambda+\frac{\pi}{N}\right) + \sin\left(\lambda-\frac{\pi}{N}\right) - \sin\frac{\pi}{N} + \sin\frac{\pi}{N}\right]\right.$$

$$\left. + \sin\frac{\pi}{N} - \sin\left(\lambda-\frac{\pi}{N}\right)\right\}$$

$$= \frac{NE_m}{2\pi}\left\{\tfrac{1}{2}\left[2\sin\lambda\cos\frac{\pi}{N}\right] + \sin\frac{\pi}{N} - \sin\lambda\cos\frac{\pi}{N} + \cos\lambda\sin\frac{\pi}{N}\right\}$$

$$= \frac{NE_m}{2\pi}\sin\frac{\pi}{N}(1+\cos\lambda) = \frac{NE_m}{\pi}\sin\frac{\pi}{N}\cos^2\frac{\lambda}{2}$$

This solution may be expressed,

$$V_d = \frac{V_0}{2}(1+\cos\lambda)$$

where V_0 = mean output voltage without overlap.

Part (b).   The moment of commutation can be delayed by grid control.

Let α = angle of delay, measured from the point of uncontrolled commutation. Referring to Fig. 101(b), mean V_d = mean of area under ABCD

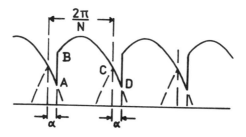

Fig. 101(b)

$\therefore$

$$\text{mean } V_d = \frac{1}{2\pi/N} \int_{(-\pi/N+\alpha)}^{(\pi/N+\alpha)} E_m \cos \theta \, d\theta$$

$$= \frac{E_m}{2\pi/N} [\sin \theta]_{(-\pi/N+\alpha)}^{(\pi/N+\alpha)}$$

$$= \frac{NE_m}{2\pi} \left[\sin \left(\frac{\pi}{N} + \alpha \right) - \sin \left(-\frac{\pi}{N} + \alpha \right) \right]$$

$$= \frac{NE_m}{\pi} \sin \frac{\pi}{N} \cos \alpha$$

This solution can be written, $V_d = V_0 \cos \alpha$.

Numerical part

$$E_m = \sqrt{2} \times 300 = 424 \text{ volt, and } \cos 20° = 0.9397$$

$$\text{Uncontrolled } V_d = V_0 = \frac{NE_m}{\pi} \sin \frac{\pi}{N} = \frac{3 \times 424 \times 0.866}{\pi}$$

$$= 351 \text{ volt}$$

For part (i),

$$V_d = \frac{V_0}{2} (1 + \cos \lambda) = \frac{351}{2} (1 + 0.9397)$$

$$= 340 \text{ volt}$$

Part (ii),

$$V_d = V_0 \cos \alpha = 351 \times 0.9397 = 329 \text{ volt}$$

Example 102

The commutation of an N-phase rectifier is retarded $\alpha°$ by grid control and has an overlap angle of $\lambda°$ due to the supply transformer inductances. Determine an expression for:

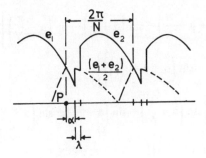

Fig. 102(a)

(a) the mean value of output voltage,
(b) the output current.
(c) Hence derive an equivalent circuit to represent the effect of overlap in terms of the transformer leakage inductances, for a 3-phase bridge rectifier.

Solution

Part (a).   Allowing for both grid control and overlap, the mean voltage is derived by integrating over the three periods as follows; (Fig. 102(a)),

$$V_d = \frac{1}{2\pi/N}\left[\int_0^\alpha e_1 \, d\theta + \int_\alpha^{\alpha+\lambda} \frac{e_1 + e_2}{2} \, d\theta + \int_{\alpha+\lambda}^{2\pi/N} e_2 \, d\theta\right]$$

Taking the point P as the origin,

$$V_d = \frac{E_m}{2\pi/N}\left[\int_0^\alpha \cos\left(\theta + \frac{\pi}{N}\right) d\theta + \frac{1}{2}\int_\alpha^{\alpha+\lambda}\left\{\cos\left(\theta + \frac{\pi}{N}\right) + \cos\left(\theta - \frac{\pi}{N}\right)\right\} d\theta\right.$$

$$\left. + \int_{\alpha+\lambda}^{2\pi/N} \cos\left(\theta - \frac{\pi}{N}\right) d\theta\right]$$

$$= \frac{NE_m}{2\pi}\left\{\left[\sin\left(\theta + \frac{\pi}{N}\right)\right]_0^\alpha + \frac{1}{2}\left[\sin\left(\theta + \frac{\pi}{N}\right) + \sin\left(\theta - \frac{\pi}{N}\right)\right]_\alpha^{\alpha+\lambda}\right.$$

$$\left. + \left[\sin\left(\theta - \frac{\pi}{N}\right)\right]_{\alpha+\lambda}^{2\pi/N}\right\}$$

$$= \frac{NE_m}{2\pi}\left\{\left[\sin\left(\alpha + \frac{\pi}{N}\right) - \sin\frac{\pi}{N}\right] + \frac{1}{2}\left[\sin\left(\alpha + \lambda + \frac{\pi}{N}\right)\right.\right.$$

$$+ \sin \left(\alpha + \lambda - \frac{\pi}{N} \right) - \sin \left(\alpha + \frac{\pi}{N} \right) - \sin \left(\alpha - \frac{\pi}{N} \right) \Bigg]$$

$$+ \left[\sin \frac{\pi}{N} - \sin \left(\alpha + \lambda - \frac{\pi}{N} \right) \right] \Bigg\} \Bigg\}$$

$$= \frac{NE_m}{2\pi} \left\{ \frac{1}{2} \left[\sin \left(\alpha + \frac{\pi}{N} \right) - \sin \left(\alpha - \frac{\pi}{N} \right) + \sin \left(\alpha + \lambda + \frac{\pi}{N} \right) \right. \right.$$

$$\left. \left. - \sin \left(\alpha + \lambda - \frac{\pi}{N} \right) \right] \right\}$$

$$= \frac{NE_m}{2\pi} \left\{ \frac{1}{2} \left[2 \cos \alpha \sin \frac{\pi}{N} + 2 \cos (\alpha + \lambda) \sin \frac{\pi}{N} \right] \right\}$$

$$= \frac{NE_m}{2\pi} \sin \frac{\pi}{N} \left[\cos \alpha + \cos (\alpha + \lambda) \right]$$

$$= \frac{V_0}{2} \left[\cos \alpha + \cos (\alpha + \lambda) \right]$$

where V_0 is the mean voltage without overlap or grid control.

Part (b). During the overlap period two anodes are conducting simultaneously and two phases of the supply transformer are effectively short-circuited. With a transformer leakage inductance/phase = L,

$$2L \frac{di}{dt} = \hat{E}_L \sin \omega t = \text{line voltage applied}$$

$$\therefore \qquad i = \frac{1}{2L} \int \hat{E}_L \sin \omega t \, d\omega t = - \frac{\hat{E}_L}{2\omega L} \cos \omega t + \text{constant}$$

At $\omega t = \alpha, i = 0$

$$\therefore \qquad\qquad \text{Constant of integration} = \frac{\hat{E}_L}{2\omega L} \cos \alpha$$

Hence

$$i = \frac{\hat{E}_L}{2X} \left[\cos \alpha - \cos \omega t \right]$$

When $\omega t = (\alpha + \lambda), i = I_d$

$$\therefore \qquad\qquad I_d = \frac{\hat{E}_L}{2X} \left[\cos \alpha - \cos (\alpha + \lambda) \right]$$

$$= \frac{E_L}{\sqrt{2} X} \left[\cos \alpha - \cos (\alpha + \lambda) \right]$$

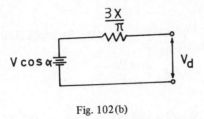

Fig. 102(b)

Part (c).   For a 3-phase bridge, $V_0 = 2$ (half-wave V_0)

$$E_L = \sqrt{3}E \quad \text{and} \quad V_0 = 2\left[\frac{\sqrt{2}E \sin \pi/3}{\pi/3}\right]$$

$$\text{or } V_0 = \frac{6}{\pi}\hat{E}_L \sin \frac{\pi}{6}, \text{both} = \frac{3\sqrt{2}}{\pi}E_L$$

$$\therefore \qquad I_d = \frac{\pi V_0}{6X}\left[\cos \alpha - \cos (\alpha + \lambda)\right]$$

Since

$$2V_d = V_0[\cos \alpha + \cos (\alpha + \lambda)],$$

from part (a) above,

$$\therefore \qquad V_d = V_0 \cos \alpha - \frac{3XI_d}{\pi} \quad \text{(see also Ref 18, p. 64)}$$

An equivalent circuit may be drawn as in Fig. 102(b) for 3-phase bridge.

Example 103

A 3-phase bridge rectifier supplies d.c. to the armature of a separately-excited d.c. motor. The motor has armature resistance of 0.12 ohm and a generated emf in volts numerically equal to 1.2 (speed in rpm). A star-connected transformer secondary winding supplies the rectifier at 580 volt/line. Neglecting rectifier volt drop and overlap effects, calculate:

(a) the firing delay angle to give a no-load speed of 500 rpm,

(b) the speed, at this firing delay, when the motor is loaded to take an armature current of 400 amp,

(c) the new firing delay angle to restore the speed to 500 rpm at the load condition,

(d) the firing delay angle when starting the motor against the same load torque.

Solution

Part (a).   For an N-phase rectifier, (see Example 99), for 3-phase bridge $N = 6$ and E_m becomes max E_L.

$$V_0 = \sqrt{2}E_L \frac{\sin \pi/N}{\pi/N}$$

$$= \sqrt{2} \times 580 \times \left(\sin \frac{\pi}{6}\right) \times \frac{6}{\pi} = 783.2 \text{ volt}$$

Rectifier output volts, at grid delay α°,

$$V_d = V_0 \cos \alpha$$

Neglecting armature volt drop on no load,

$$1.2(500) = 600 = 783.2 \cos \alpha$$

$\therefore$ $\alpha = \cos^{-1}(600/783.2) = 40^\circ$

Part (b).   On load,

Hence   armature $I_a R_a = 400 \times 0.12 = 48$ volts.

motor emf $= 600 - 48 = 552$ volt

$\therefore$ Motor speed $= \dfrac{552}{1.2} = 460$ rpm

Part (c).   Required $V_d = 600 + 48 = 648$ volt

$\therefore$ New $\alpha = \cos^{-1}(648/783.2) = \cos^{-1} 0.8273$

$$= 34^\circ 11'$$

Part (d).   At standstill, $V_d = 48$ volt

$\therefore$ Required $\alpha = \cos^{-1}(48/783.2) = \cos^{-1} 0.0613$

$$= 86^\circ 29'$$

Example 104

A 3-phase bridge rectifier, employing grid-controlled rectifiers, operates normally to supply a d.c. load having large inductance. The input is a sinusoidal balanced 3-phase voltage of line value E_1.

(a) Show that a limit for rectifier operation occurs when $K \leqslant 2 \cos \alpha$, where K is a current factor $= (\sqrt{2}X_c I_d/E_1)$, and $\alpha =$ delay angle of the firing pulse, $X_c =$ commutating reactance.

(b) Examine the limit as applied to inverter operation.

Solution

Part (a). Large values of K indicate excessive I_d and/or reduced E_1. Now, in general for a N-phase rectifier, (ref. Example 99)

$$V_0 = \frac{N}{\pi} E_m \sin \frac{\pi}{N} = \frac{N}{\pi} \sqrt{2} E \sin \frac{\pi}{N}$$

where E = rms volts/phase.

For $N = 3$ phases, (bridge $V_0 = 2 \times$ half-wave V_0)

$$\tfrac{1}{2} V_0 = \frac{3}{\pi} \sqrt{2} E \sin \frac{\pi}{3} = \frac{3}{\pi} \sqrt{2} E \left(\frac{\sqrt{3}}{2} \right)$$

$$= \frac{3E_1}{\sqrt{2}\pi}$$

Then we have,

$$V_d = \frac{V_0}{2} [\cos \alpha + \cos (\alpha + \lambda)], \text{ (ref. Example 102)}$$

$$= \frac{3E_1}{\sqrt{2}\pi} [\cos \alpha + \cos (\alpha + \lambda)]$$

Also,

$$I_d = \frac{\pi V_0}{6X_c} [\cos \alpha - \cos (\alpha + \lambda)]$$

$$= \frac{E_1}{\sqrt{2}X_c} [\cos \alpha - \cos (\alpha + \lambda)]$$

$$\therefore \quad K = \frac{\sqrt{2}X_c I_d}{E_1} = [\cos \alpha - \cos (\alpha + \lambda)]$$

and,

$$\cos (\alpha + \lambda) = \cos \alpha - K$$

Substituting above,

$$V_d = \frac{3E_1}{\sqrt{2}\pi} (2 \cos \alpha - K)$$

A limit for rectifier operation occurs when $V_d = 0$. Hence $K \leqslant (2 \cos \alpha)$ is the condition.

N.B. Normal operation means no overlap of commutations and $\lambda \leqslant 60°$. Then, substituting above we have,

$$K = \cos \alpha - \cos (\alpha + 60°)$$

$$= \cos \alpha - [\cos \alpha \cos 60° - \sin \alpha \sin 60°]$$

$$= \cos \alpha - \tfrac{1}{2} \cos \alpha + \sin \alpha \sin 60°$$

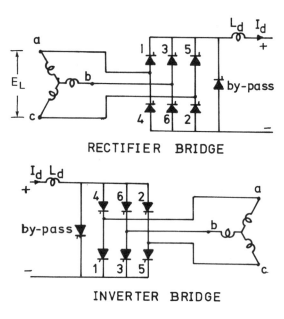

RECTIFIER   BRIDGE

INVERTER   BRIDGE

Fig. 104

$$= \tfrac{1}{2} \cos \alpha + \sin \alpha \sin 60°$$

$$= \cos 60° \cos \alpha + \sin 60° \sin \alpha$$

$$= \cos (60° - \alpha)$$

Part (b).   For a 3-phase bridge rectifer, when α is increased beyond $60°$ there will be some negative voltage. If the load is resistance the operation would be intermittent, since reverse conduction is not possible. When a large reactor is provided, the difference between $-ve$ and $+ve$ voltage areas gives a resultant voltage output on the d.c. side. Now if an external d.c. voltage is applied which overcomes this $-ve$ area, current will flow from anode to cathode, in opposition to induced voltage in the transformer secondaries, thus indicating power to the a.c. system.

Inverter operation is thus mathematically similar to rectifier operation, except that commutation must be completed and the outgoing valve has time to de-ionise before anode voltage causes re-ignition.

Because of the 'mirror-image' nature of the inverter waveforms, rectifier equations, suitably modified, can be applied. We define,

$$\beta = \text{inverter angle of advance} = (180° - \alpha)$$

$$\delta = \text{inverter extinction angle} = 180° - (\alpha + \lambda)$$

Thus for an inverter,

$$-V_d = \frac{V_0}{2}[\cos\beta + \cos\delta]$$

Also

$$-V_d = V_0\cos\beta + \frac{3X_cI_d}{\pi}$$

Substituting in terms of rectifier angles, α and λ,

$$V_d = \frac{V_0}{2}[\cos\alpha + \cos(\alpha + \lambda)]$$

and

$$V_d = V_0\cos\alpha - \frac{3X_cI_d}{\pi}$$

Hence,

$$\cos\alpha + \cos(\alpha + \lambda) = 2\cos\alpha - \left(\frac{2\times3X_cI_d}{\pi}\right)\left(\frac{\pi}{3\sqrt{2}E_1}\right)$$

Rearranging we get,

$$K = \cos\alpha - \cos(\alpha + \lambda)$$

$$\lambda = \cos^{-1}[\cos\alpha - K] - \alpha$$

Thus

$$V_d = \frac{V_0}{2}[2\cos\alpha - K]$$

Hence a limit for inverter operation is given when $V_d = 0$, or

$$K > 2\cos\alpha.$$

N.B. V_d is a negative quantity.

(See Ref. Paper 3 for an extended treatment.)

Example 105

Derive an expression for the load current during the conduction period of a single-phase half-wave rectifier, supplying a series R–L load, from a sinusoidal a.c. supply. Sketch the approximate waveforms of current and voltage for the condition $R/\omega L = \sqrt{3}$. Estimate the instants of peak and zero current. Discuss d.c. motor control by controlled rectifier.

Solution

Let the supply voltage, $v = V_m \sin\omega t$. During conduction,

$$v = L\,di/dt + iR$$

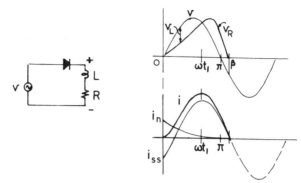

Fig. 105 (a)

Now $i = i_{ss} + i_n$ where $i_{ss} =$ steady-state value, $i_n =$ transient part. For an inductive circuit at steady-state, current lags by ϕ, where

Then,
$$\tan \phi = \omega L/R \quad \text{and} \quad Z = [R^2 + (\omega L)^2]^{1/2}$$

$$i_{ss} = \frac{V_m}{Z} \sin (\omega t - \phi)$$

The transient part can be written, $i_n = A\, \epsilon^{-t/T}$ where $T = L/R$.
Now at $t = 0, i = 0$, and substituting above to determine A,

Hence,
$$0 = \frac{-V_m \sin \phi}{Z} + A \quad \text{whence} \quad A = \frac{V_m \sin \phi}{Z}$$

$$i = \frac{V_m}{Z} [\sin (\omega t - \phi) + \epsilon^{-t/T} \sin \phi] \quad \text{(see Fig. 105(a))}$$

Differentiating to determine the condition for maximum;

$$di/dt = \frac{V_m}{Z} \left[\omega \cos (\omega t - \phi) - \frac{1}{T} \epsilon^{-t/T} \sin \phi \right]$$

Given $R/\omega L = \sqrt{3}$, then $T = 1/(\sqrt{3}\omega)$ and $\phi = 30° = \pi/6$ rad. We may neglect the exponential term, (Fig. 105(a)) and for max. we have (approx),

Then
$$\cos (\omega t - \phi) = 0$$

$$(\omega t - \phi) = \pi/2$$

Since $\phi = \pi/6$, max. current occurs at t_1, where

$$\omega t_1 = \frac{\pi}{2} + \frac{\pi}{6} = \frac{2\pi}{3}$$

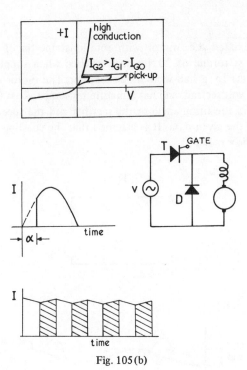

Fig. 105(b)

Also, the 'extinction angle',

$$\beta = \pi + \frac{\pi}{6} = \frac{7\pi}{6} \quad \text{(see Fig. 105(a))}$$

Second part. Typical silicon-controlled-rectifier, (S.C.R. or 'thyristor') characteristics show that 'gate' control determines the 'firing' angle, α, when the rectifying device begins to conduct, (Fig. 105(b)). The gate is triggered by a secondary circuit. The d.c. motor is supplied with a 'chopped' d.c. and the mean current to the machine is controlled by the frequency and duration of the pulses.

Figure 105(b) shows a simplified waveform, where the shaded parts are the current supply to the machine. Current decay to the machine is controlled by the back emf, and extended periods of conduction are affected by stored energy in the inductance of the machine, as demonstrated in the passive $R–L$ circuit example. Addition of the 'flywheel' diode, (D), permits prolonged flow of machine current during cut-off of the thyristor (T), and enables inductive energy to be dissipated.

Multi-phase operation minimises the 'dip' in machine speed which will occur due to fluctuation in the current supply.

Example 106

A separately-excited d.c. motor with rotational inertia of $J = 0.03\,\text{kg}\,\text{m}^2$, develops a gross torque of 20 Nm at 50 rad/sec when supplied from 240 V 50 Hz a.c. mains by a half-wave diode rectifier. The motor constant, $K_m =$ 3.61 Nm/A or volt sec/rad, and has armature resistance, $R_a = 0.585$ ohm. It is required to find the firing angle of the rectifier and the speed fluctuation of the motor for the given data. It is assumed that the coasting period between current pulses is π radian.

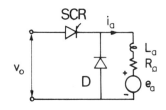

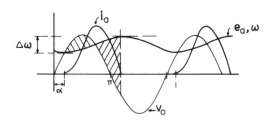

Fig. 106 (a, b)

Solution.   (Ref. 3, p. 402)

During conduction, (Fig. 106(a))

$$v = i_a R_a + L_a \, di_a/dt + e_a$$

where e_a = machine back emf.

Current, i_a flows when $v > e_a$, with i_a increasing. When $e_a > v$, i_a decreases and $L \, di_a/dt$ changes sign, thereby aiding continued flow of i_a and such that average $L \, di/dt$ over the conduction period is zero, (the shaded areas are equal, Fig. 106(b)).

The torque of electrical origin, $\text{(T)}_e = K_m i_a$ accelerates J and drives the shaft load, (T)_L. Thus

$$\widehat{T}_e = J\frac{d}{dt} + \widehat{T}_L$$

Averaged over a period, $\widehat{T}_e = \widehat{T}_L = K_m i_a$.

First part.   From given data, conduction occurs from α to $(\pi + \alpha)$ and coasting from $(\pi + \alpha)$ to $(2\pi + \alpha)$ etc.

Let $v = V_m \sin \theta$. Average applied volts over conduction period,

$$V_{av} = \frac{1}{\pi} \int_\alpha^{\pi+\alpha} \sqrt{2} V \sin \theta \, d\theta \quad \text{where } V = \text{RMS value.}$$

$$= -\frac{\sqrt{2}}{\pi} V [\cos \theta]_\alpha^{\pi+\alpha}$$

$$= -\frac{\sqrt{2}}{\pi} V [\cos (\pi + \alpha) - \cos \alpha]$$

$$= \frac{2\sqrt{2}}{\pi} V \cos \alpha$$

$$= \omega_0 K_m + I_a' R_a$$

where

$$\omega_0 = \text{av. speed}$$

$$I_a' = \text{av. } I_a \text{ over conduction period}$$

$$\text{Av. } I_a \text{ over a cycle} = \frac{\widehat{T}_e}{K_m} = \frac{20}{3.61} = 5.55 \text{ amp}$$

Then

$$\text{Av. } I_a' \text{ (over a conduction period)} = 2 \times 5.55 = 11.1 \text{ amp}$$

$$V_{av} = (50 \times 3.61) + (11.1 \times 0.585)$$

$$= 180.5 + 6.5 = 187$$

$$= \frac{2\sqrt{2}}{\pi} V \cos \alpha$$

$V = 240$ (given)

$\therefore$

$$\cos \alpha = \frac{\pi}{2\sqrt{2}} \frac{187}{240} = 0.86$$

Firing angle,

$$\alpha = 30°$$

Second part.   From graph (Fig. 106(b)),

$$e_a \text{ (min)} = V_m \sin \alpha$$

$$= \sqrt{2} V \sin \alpha = \sqrt{2} \times 240 \times \sin 30°$$

$$= 169.68$$

$$= K_m(\omega_{min})$$

$\therefore$ Minimum $\omega = \dfrac{169.68}{3.61} = 47.0$ rad/sec

During coasting,

$$J\,d\omega/dt - \textcircled{T}_e = 0$$

or

$$J\,d\omega/dt - B\omega = 0 \quad \text{where} \quad B = \frac{\textcircled{T}_e}{\omega}$$

i.e., stored energy is absorbed by load.

General solution for speed,

$$\omega = \omega_1 \epsilon^{-t/\tau_L}$$

where $\omega_1 = $ initial speed and $\tau_L = J/B = $ mech. time constant

Speed fluctuation $= \Delta\omega = \dfrac{d\omega}{dt}t_c$

where $t_c = $ coasting time

$$= (\omega_{max} - \omega_{min})$$

$$\omega_{min} = \omega_{max}\left(1 - \frac{t_c}{\tau_L}\epsilon^{-t_c/\tau_L}\right)$$

We have

$$B = \frac{\textcircled{T}_e}{\omega} = \frac{20}{50} = 0.4 \quad \text{and} \quad \tau_L = J/B = \frac{0.03}{0.4} = 0.075$$

$$t_c = \frac{\pi}{2\pi f} = 0.01 \text{ sec}$$

Hence

$$\Delta\omega = \frac{0.01}{0.075}\epsilon^{-0.01/0.075} = 0.133\,\epsilon^{-0.133}$$

$$= 0.133 \times 0.87 = 11.6\%$$

Example 107

A half-wave diode rectifier is employed to charge a 36 V battery from a 240 V 50 Hz transformer supply. The resistance of the charging circuit in the forward direction is 200 ohm. Working from first principles, it is required to estimate the charging rate in ampere-hours per 24 hours. Discuss a bridge alternative.

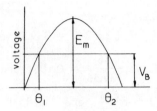

Fig. 107(a)

Solution

Referring to diagram, Fig. 107(a)

Charging occurs between θ_1 and θ_2;

Forward volts $= E_m \sin \theta - V_B$.

From diagram, $V_B = E_m \sin \theta_1$,   and $\sin \theta_1 = \dfrac{V_B}{E_m}$

Taking E_m as reference,

Charging circuit forward volts (average)/$\frac{1}{2}$ cycle

$$= \frac{1}{\pi} \int_{-(\pi/2-\theta_1)}^{(\pi/2-\theta_1)} (E_m \cos \theta - V_B)\, d\theta$$

$$= \frac{1}{\pi} [E_m \sin \theta - \theta V_B]_{-(\pi/2-\theta_1)}^{(\pi/2-\theta_1)}$$

$$= \frac{1}{\pi} [2E_m \sin (\pi/2 - \theta_1) - \pi V_B]$$

$$= \frac{2E_m}{\pi} \sin (\pi/2 - \theta_1) - V_B$$

I_{av}/cycle $= \frac{1}{2}[I_{av}/\frac{1}{2}$ cycle]   for half-wave operation.

$$= \frac{1}{2R} \left[\frac{2E_m}{\pi} \sin (\pi/2 - \theta_1) - V_B \right]$$

where

R = forward circuit resistance

= transformer resistance, $(R_2 + k^2 R_1)$ + diode forward resistance

+ battery resistance

Numerical part

$$E_m = \sqrt{2} \times 240 = 339.36 \text{ volt}$$

$$\sin \theta_1 = V_B/E_m = \frac{36}{339.36} = 0.106 \quad \text{and} \quad \theta_1 = 6.1°$$

Then

$$(\pi/2 - \theta_1) = 83.9° \quad \text{and} \quad \sin 83.9° = 0.994$$

Hence,

$$I_{av}/\text{cycle} = \frac{1}{2 \times 200}\left[\left(\frac{2 \times 339.36}{\pi} \times 0.994\right) - 36\right]$$

$$= \frac{1}{400}(214.74 - 36)$$

$$= 0.45 \text{ A/cycle.}$$

$$\text{Ampere-hours/24 hours} = 0.45 \times 24 = 10.8 \text{ Ah}$$

N.B.   In practice an added control rheostat permits,
   (i) control of charging current as per specification, and
   (ii) adjustment for battery voltage during charge, per 2 V cell, say 1.75 V (uncharged) to 2.6 V (fully charged).

Last part

The following analysis highlights important features of battery charging circuit design, (Fig. 107(b)).

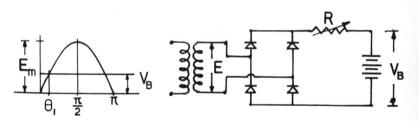

Fig. 107(b)

We may write, charging current, $i = \dfrac{1}{R}(E_m \sin \theta - V_B)$

$$i^2 = \frac{1}{R^2}(E_m^2 \sin^2\theta - 2V_B E_m \sin \theta + V_B^2)$$

Mean i^2 may be obtained by integrating between θ_1 and $\pi/2$, thus,

$$\text{mean } i^2 = \frac{2}{\pi R^2} \int_{\theta_1}^{\pi/2} [E_m^2 \sin^2\theta - 2V_B E_m \sin\theta + V_B^2] \, d\theta$$

$$= \frac{2}{\pi R^2} \int_{\theta_1}^{\pi/2} \left[\frac{E_m^2}{2}(1 - \cos 2\theta) - 2V_B E_m \sin\theta + V_B^2\right] d\theta$$

$$= \frac{2}{\pi R^2}\left[\frac{E_m^2}{2}(\theta + \tfrac{1}{2}\sin 2\theta) - 2V_B E_m \cos\theta + V_B^2\theta\right]_{\theta_1}^{\pi/2}$$

$$= \frac{2}{\pi R^2}\left[\frac{E_m^2}{2}\left\{\left(\frac{\pi}{2} + \tfrac{1}{2}\sin\pi\right) - (\theta_1 + \tfrac{1}{2}\sin 2\theta_1)\right\}\right.$$

$$\left. - 2V_B E_m\left(\cos\frac{\pi}{2} - \cos\theta_1\right) + V_B^2\left(\frac{\pi}{2} - \theta_1\right)\right]$$

$$\doteq \frac{2}{\pi R^2}\left[\frac{E_m^2}{2}\left(\frac{\pi}{2} - \theta_1 - \tfrac{1}{2}\sin 2\theta_1\right) + 2V_B E_m \cos\theta_1 + V_B^2\left(\frac{\pi}{2} - \theta_1\right)\right]$$

Substituting given values, $E_m = 339.36$, $V_B = 36$, $\theta_1 = 6.1° = 0.1065$ rad and $R = 200$, as above, gives

$$\text{mean } i^2 \text{ (full-wave)} = 0.159 \times 10^{-4}(78\,192 + 24\,287 + 1821)$$

$$= 1.658 \left(\text{or } \frac{1.658}{2} = 0.829 \text{ half-wave}\right)$$

Hence

$I_{RMS}(\text{bridge}) = \sqrt{1.658} = 1.29$ amp   (compared with $I_{av} = 0.9$)

$I_{RMS}(\text{half-wave}) = \sqrt{0.829} = 0.91$ amp   (compared with $I_{av} = 0.45$)

This means that the power rating of the Control Resistance

(i) for half-wave case, must by $0.829/(0.45)^2 = 4.09$ times a rating mistakenly judged on the mean charging current.

(ii) for the bridge case, the ratio is $1.658/(0.9)^2 = 2.05$ times.

To determine the alternative bridge rectifier to supply a mean charging current of 0.45 A; from the first part, (neglecting source and rectifier impedances),

$$200 \times 0.45 = \frac{2E_m}{\pi}\left(\sin\frac{\pi}{2} - \theta_1\right) - V_B$$

$$90 = \frac{2E_m}{\pi}\cos\theta_1 - 36$$

$$\therefore \qquad E_m \cos\theta_1 = \frac{126\pi}{2} = 197.92$$

Now

$$E_m \sin \theta_1 = V_B = 36$$

$$\therefore \qquad \tan \theta_1 = \frac{36}{197.92} = 0.1819$$

$$\theta_1 = 10.3° = 0.18 \text{ rad}$$

$$E_m = \frac{V_B}{\sin \theta_1} = \frac{36}{0.1788} = 203.39 \text{ volt}$$

$$E_{RMS} = 178.26 \text{ volt}$$

Also

Mean i^2 (new bridge) $= 0.159 \times 10^{-4} (25\,130.75 + 14\,395.13 + 1801.44)$

$$= 0.6571$$

$$I_{RMS} = 0.81 \text{ amp}$$

Note   The VA rating of the new transformer

$$= 0.81 \times 178.26$$

$$= 144.39 \text{ VA}$$

Compare with the transformer for the half-wave case

$$= 0.91 \times 240$$

$$= 218.4 \text{ VA}$$

The comparative power rating of the Control Resistance on the basis shown above, is $0.6571/(0.45)^2 = 3.25$ times.

The Bridge Rectifier is therefore to be preferred. The fact that 4 rectifier components are required is not a problem since they are very inexpensive.

References

Books

1. Hammond, P., *Electromagnetism for Engineers*, Pergamon Press, Oxford (1964).
2. Steven, R. E., *Electromechanics and Machines*, Chapman & Hall, London (1970).
3. Fitzgerald, Kingsley and Kusko, *Electric Machinery*, McGraw-Hill, New York, 3rd ed. (1971).
4. Say, M. G., *Alternating Current Machines*, Pitmans, London (1976).
5. Adkins, B., *The General Theory of Electrical Machines*, Chapman and Hall, London (1962).
6. Hindmarsh, J., *Electrical Machines*, Pergamon Press, Oxford (1965).
7. Weedy, B. M., *Electric Power Systems*, Wiley, New York, 2nd ed. (reprint, 1975).
8. Rissik, H., *Mercury Arc Current Convertors*, Pitmans, London, 2nd ed. (1963).
9. Adamson and Hingorani, *H.V. Direct Current Power Transmission*, Garraway, London (1960).
10. Cory, B. J., *H.V. Direct Current Converters and Systems*, Macdonald, London (1965).
11. Waller, W. F. (Editor), *Rectifier Circuits*, Macmillan Press Ltd., Basingstoke, Hampshire, U.K. (1972).
12. Waddicor, H., *The Principles of Electric Power Transmission*, Chapman and Hall, London (1948).
13. Hancock, N. N., *Matrix Analysis of Electrical Machinery*, Pergamon Press, Oxford (1964).
14. Jones, D., *Analysis and Protection of Electrical Power Systems*, Pitmans, London (1971).
15. Chard, F. de la C., *Electricity Supply*, Longman Press, London (1976).
6. Stevenson, W. D., *Elements of Power System Analysis*, McGraw-Hill, New York (1962).
7. *The International System of Units*, H.M. Stationery Office, London (1970).
8. Davis, Rex M., *Power diode and thyristor circuits*, IEE Monograph Series 7, Peter Peregrinus Ltd. Stevenage, England (1976).

Papers

1. Allen, T. P., 'Modified Circle Diagram', *Electrical Times*, No. 2794, Vol. 107, 1945, pp. 567–8.
2. Steven, R. E., 'Analysis of an Electromechanical Transducer', *Int. Journ. Elect. Engng. Educ.*, Vol. 8, No. 5, 1970, pp. 395–399.
3. Giesner, D. B. and Arrillaga, J., 'Operating Modes of the 3-phase Bridge Convertor', *Int. Journ. Elect. Engng. Educ.*, Vol. 8, No. 5, 1970, pp. 373–388.
4. Steven, R. E., 'Limitations of The Analogy', *Int. Journ. Elect. Engng. Educ.*, Vol. 13, pp. 197–201 (1976).
5. Schade, O. H., 'Analysis of Rectifier Operation', *Proc. I.R.E.*, July, 1943, p. 341 *et seq.*

Index